Mr. Justice Black
and His Books

Mr. Justice Black in the study
of his Alexandria, Virginia, home.
(The *New York Times*, January 24, 1970)

Mr. Justice Black

and His Books

Daniel J. Meador

University Press of Virginia

Charlottesville

To my children

Barrie, Anna, Dan

Contents

Illustrations

Preface

The principal feature of this book is the catalogue of Mr. Justice Black's personal library, compiled directly from the books which were in his home and Supreme Court chambers at his death in September, 1971. The catalogue, which excludes law books, contains 953 titles. Some are multi-volume works, so the actual number of books in the collection is considerably larger. The task of constructing such a catalogue, verifying and supplementing the bibliographical information, and preparing this kind of manuscript for publication is indeed substantial. It has been accomplished through the labors of several persons to whom I—and future generations—are indebted. To them I acknowledge my appreciation:

Elizabeth S. Black, widow of the Justice, who assisted in the listing of the books, provided access to the Justice's study, furnished valuable information, and in many other ways cooperated in the venture.

Mary S. Burdick, of the University of Virginia Law Class of 1973, who did bibliographical research and proofreading, typed a large portion of the catalogue, and served as a perceptive editorial critic.

Gwendolyn B. Folsom, of the University of Virginia Law School research staff, who did the major part of the initial cataloguing of the books with her characteristic thoroughness and gave essential bibliographical and editorial advice.

Eleanor H. Kett, my secretary and assistant, who carried out extensive bibliographical research, typed substantial portions of the catalogue, proofread the manuscript, and assisted in a multitude of ways in getting this book to press.

Frances L. Lamb, last secretary to Mr. Justice Black, who assisted in the listing of the books and provided a variety of helpful information.

In addition, I am grateful to Professor Carl McFarland of the University of Virginia Law School, director of the Virginia Legal Studies series, who gave encouragement and backing for this project from the outset and provided valuable editorial suggestions. I am grateful also to Hardy C. Dillard, former Dean of the University of Virginia Law School, now Judge of the International Court of Justice, for reading a draft of the essay and tendering his typically helpful commentary.

Appreciation is due to Hugo L. Black, Jr., son of the Justice, for his cooperation in allowing access to the books, for commenting on a draft of the introductory essay, and for furnishing information.

The introductory essay draws heavily on the personal, unpublished recollections of Justice Black's former law clerks. Those young law graduates who came and went, for one or two years each, over the thirty-four years he was on the Court saw better than others what Justice Black's books meant to him and which of his many books he liked best and considered most significant. They had a unique vantage point because of their close, day-to-day associations with the Justice.[1] The role of books in the clerking experience stands out in the memory of nearly all.

In the essay I have not attempted to identify the specific source of all the statements made. Suffice it to say that unless indicated otherwise, the essay is based on information supplied by persons mentioned above, my own recollections and recent examination of the books, and information derived from the collective memory of the following law clerks: Kenneth C. Bass, III, Guido Calabresi, David M. Clark, Melford O. Cleveland, Jerome A. Cooper, C. Sam Daniels, Walter E. Dellinger, III, Floyd F. Feeney, John P. Frank, George C. Freeman, Jr., William Joslin, John G. Kester, Charles F. Luce, Robert B. McCaw, John K. McNulty, Drayton Nabers, Jr., James L. North, Covert Eugene Parnell, III, Joseph H. Price, George L. Saunders, Jr., Stephen J. Schulhofer, Robert W. Spearman, David J. Vann, and Frank M. Wozencraft. However, no one other than myself should be held responsible for what I have ultimately chosen to say in the essay.

Messrs. Cleveland and Kester, in addition to furnishing especially useful information, each read a draft of the essay and offered helpful suggestions.

The preparation of this volume has been a pleasant undertaking, recalling many happy hours and intellectually absorbing experiences. To be once again in Justice Black's study browsing in his favorite books has been to relive an extraordinarily fascinating year of long ago. In these books he still seems very much alive. My hope is that this will be an historically useful work on Hugo Black and at the same time a testimonial to the practical and timeless importance of great literature.

DANIEL J. MEADOR

The University of Virginia
April, 1973

[1] A complete list, by term of Court, of all fifty-three of Justice Black's law clerks appears at page 197. Something of the relationships among the law clerks and Black can be gathered from a collection of vignettes, one by each clerk, entitled *Confessions of the Law Clerks—Extracted for the 80th Birthday of Mr. Justice Black—February 27, 1966* (privately printed, 1966). See also Meador, Justice Black and His Law Clerks, 15 *Ala. L. Rev.* 57 (1962).

Mr. Justice Black
and His Books

I venture to believe that it is as important to a judge called upon to pass on a question of constitutional law, to have at least a bowing acquaintance with Acton and Maitland, with Thucydides, Gibbon and Carlyle, with Homer, Dante, Shakespeare and Milton, with Machiavelli, Montaigne and Rabelais, with Plato, Bacon, Hume and Kant, as with the books which have been specifically written on the subject. For in such matters everything turns upon the spirit in which he approaches the questions before him.

—Learned Hand (1930)

He [a great judge] must have a full sense of the seamless web of life, a grasp of the endless tradition from which we cannot escape. He must be capable of stern logic, and yet refuse to sacrifice to logic the hopes and fears and wants of men. He must be able to catch a glimpse of the ultimate in the immediate, of the universal in the particular.

—Harold Laski (1939)

Mr. Justice Black and His Books

BOOKS played a significant role in the life of Justice Hugo L. Black. Through his love of reading he acquired the kind of familiarity with the great writings which Learned Hand viewed, in an often-quoted passage, as essential for a judge who passes on questions of constitutional law.[1] Instinctively, and perhaps consciously, Justice Black sensed that reading along those lines was necessary to develop the qualities of mind which Harold Laski associated with the "great judge."[2] Though reading and acquiring books are, of course, not uncommon among judges and lawyers, Justice Black and his books present a distinctive picture. There was a uniqueness about his reading habits, his reading interests, and his collection of books. And there was a uniqueness in the way that historical literature colored his views of contemporaneous affairs.

Justice Black's reading reveals one of the contrasts in his life. For though he was an avid reader, he had not been nurtured in a strongly intellectual environment. Moreover, during the first half of his career he was primarily a man of action, a trial lawyer, a politician, and a United States Senator. Yet he found time, long before entering the quieter world of the Supreme Court, to explore literature far beyond the currently topical. He would not, though, have been considered a bookworm. On the contrary, he liked people, and he had a memorable personality, a rich mixture of the serious and the humorous, the hard and the soft, a personality formed through a lifetime's experiences in markedly different times and places.

Born in 1886 in a world without automobiles, electricity, or radio, he lived into the age of jet travel, nuclear fission, television, and walks on the moon. Remembering the nineteenth century, he saw as an adult the two world wars of the twentieth century, the great depression, the wars in Korea and Vietnam, and the advent of the welfare state and the technological revolution. Eight men served as President during his time in Washington. And on the Supreme Court he sat with five Chief Justices. Through these tumultuous decades, beset with change, in much of which

[1] Hand, *The Spirit of Liberty* 81 (Dilliard ed., New York: Alfred A. Knopf, 1952), quoted herein at p. xii.

[2] Laski, *The Danger of Being a Gentleman* 228 (London: George Allen and Unwin, 1939), quoted herein at p. xii. This passage is underlined in Black's copy of this book.

he played a part, he read the literature of the past. Despite the changes and contrasts he encountered, he saw in that literature and in the world around him a timelessness about human problems and a relatively un-changing picture of human nature.

Black's interest in reading led him to assemble a sizable personal library in the course of nearly half a century as United States Senator and Supreme Court Justice. He wanted to own and to mark and to reread those books which meant something special to him. No serious study of Black's public career could ignore his books and the role they played in his life. The catalogue published here will enable all who are interested to know precisely what books made up this collection.

As an introduction to the catalogue, this essay is intended to provide information about Justice Black's reading interests and reading habits, to identify his favorite writings, and to indicate something of how he viewed them. The essay may be useful as a source of background in-formation and guidance, not otherwise available, for those who wish to examine the books themselves, and thereby to gain a better understand-ing of the mind of Justice Black. But it does not purport to analyze the influence of these books specifically on Black's Supreme Court decisions; that would require a substantial study in itself and is beyond the scope of this volume.

The Education of a Reader

In 1929 Will Durant published an article in the *American Magazine* entitled "One Hundred Best Books."[3] That was three years after Hugo Black's election to the United States Senate. Black cut out the article and kept it on hand the rest of his life. It was a splendidly written piece, exuding a love of good books similar in spirit to that which Black often voiced. With the investment of an hour a day, the article asserted, a person could read the hundred books over a four-year period, thereby becoming "better educated than any new-fledged Doctor of Philosophy in the land." Durant listed the books in twelve groups; he gave an elo-quent overview of the sweep of history and ideas which the reader would encounter as he progressed from one group to the next. Among the groupings were Greece, Rome, Europe in the seventeenth, the eigh-teenth, and the nineteenth centuries, and America. Many of the volumes listed in the article can be found in the catalogue published here.

The nature and date of Durant's article, and the fact that Black kept it, buttress the often-told story that Black launched into an intensified

[3] Durant, One Hundred Best Books, *American Magazine*, Dec. 1929, p. 26.

reading of history and philosophy after his initial election to the Senate in 1926. The Durant reading program is indeed similar to that which Black is said to have pursued from that time forward, especially during his first term as a Senator. A further bit of evidence from that same period is a clipping kept by Black from a Birmingham newspaper of 1927, in which the Birmingham Public Library listed "100 Worthwhile Books."[4]

The books and types of books Black read over the ten years after 1926 are revealed by two sources. One is the biography by John Frank, a former law clerk;[5] the other is an article by Clifford Durr, who knew Black personally from his pre-Senate days to his death.[6] Both Frank and Durr say that Black read several hundred volumes during his Senate years. Their illustrative samplings are similar. According to their reports, in the early part of this period Black read Adam Smith's *Wealth of Nations*, Draper's *History of the Intellectual Development of Europe*, and Charles Beard's *An Economic Interpretation of the Constitution*. He then worked his way through writings by Franklin, Hamilton, John Adams, Montesquieu, Rousseau, Locke, Bryce, Mill, Marx, Spencer, Veblen, Aristotle, Spinoza, St. Thomas Aquinas, St. Augustine, Herodotus, Thucydides, Plutarch, Seneca, Cicero, Virgil, Shakespeare, Milton, Hawthorne, Thoreau, and Mark Twain. He covered the records of the federal constitutional convention and of the state ratifying conventions, histories of the Supreme Court, and numerous biographies. He read or reread almost all writings by Thomas Jefferson. Later he reached William James and John Dewey.

The effect of this reading was registered on Charles Beard when he first met Black at a small Washington dinner gathering in 1934. Though Beard did not realize Black's identity until the evening was over, he had become impressed with him, through their conversation, as a man who "had read widely in history, American and European, and made scholarly excursions on his own account . . . a man imbued with a sense of history and more eager to explore than to dogmatize."[7]

Biographical sketches of Black often emphasize the reading which he undertook after his election to the Senate. There has also been a popular notion that he was "self-educated." The result has been to minimize

[4] *Birmingham Age Herald*, Aug. 20, 1927. The clipping was stuck in Black's copy of de Tocqueville, *Democracy in America*. Will Durant's article was kept in a drawer in his study.

[5] Frank, *Mr. Justice Black, the Man and His Opinions* 45–47 (1949).

[6] Durr, Hugo L. Black: A Personal Appraisal, 6 *Ga. L. Rev.* 1, 6 (1971). Durr and Black married sisters.

[7] Frank, *Mr. Justice Black, the Man and His Opinions* xi–xii (New York: Alfred A. Knopf, 1949).

unduly his reading before that time as well as his educational background generally. The facts are that Black had received a formal education enjoyed by only a small percentage of the population in his time and that he had been reading long before his Senate days. Though he grew up in the obscurity of the hill country of Alabama where there was less of a tradition of university education than in the older and wealthier regions of the state, he was not reared in a poverty-stricken or illiterate family. His father was a relatively prosperous merchant; his older brother was a medical doctor who had attended the University of the South at Sewanee. Black himself, as a teen-ager, attended Ashland College, a nineteenth-century version of what would now be thought of as a combination high school and junior college. There he took courses in literature, logic, Latin, Greek, and rhetoric.[8] He undoubtedly had exposure to classical writings, as they were staple academic fare in institutions of that sort at the turn of the century. Later, while in law school at the University of Alabama, he attended classes in history, political economy, and English. He looked back on this experience as increasing his interest in history and stimulating a new interest in political economy. It was then, he wrote years later, that he became fascinated with ancient Greece.[9] His published reminiscences convey the impression that his classes outside the law school meant as much to him intellectually as the study of law, and perhaps more in the long run.

Thus by the time Hugo Black finished law school in 1906 and entered practice he had been afforded more than a modest exposure to the great literature and ideas of Western civilization. Intellectual seeds had been planted in a mind where they could grow. Better formal education might have been available elsewhere in the United States. But it is erroneous to think of Black as an unlettered countryman who, without benefit of schooling, was introduced to good literature for the first time at the age of forty.

Yet it is true, as the *Nation* commented in 1937 at the time of his Court appointment, that Black "did not have in his blood and at his command the traditions of intellectual enlightenment" which Holmes and Cardozo inherited; he "had no one like Emerson near him to discuss Plato with, as Holmes did, no expensive Harvard training as Brandeis did."[10] But despite the lack of those advantages, Black, in the middle nineteen twenties, was seen to be "a highly educated man" by Clifford Durr, then a recent Rhodes Scholar and a young lawyer in Birmingham. Durr has said that by the time of Black's election to the Senate he already had

[8] Black, Reminiscences, 18 *Ala. L. Rev.* 3 (1965).
[9] *Id.* at 7.
[10] *The Nation*, Oct. 2, 1937, p. 337.

read "a surprising amount of history, economics, political science, and even philosophy," and had also read nearly everything by or about Thomas Jefferson.[11] A recent biography tells of an earlier time, around 1913, when Black and his partner, as young bachelor lawyers, would read aloud at night from Gibbon's *The History of the Decline and Fall of the Roman Empire*.[12] According to another biography, Black had been pursuing a reading program ever since graduation from law school.[13]

From all the evidence a picture emerges of an energetic, intelligent lawyer, with a well above average educational start for his day, who read on his own more seriously and more widely than most lawyers in his time, and who substantially intensified and expanded his reading after coming to Washington as a new United States Senator.

That Black turned out to be well read and to have a genuine knowledge of history and literature was, and continues to be, surprising to many. After all, in Washington and elsewhere, not much is expected of an Alabama politician. After Black went on the Court, talk of his having been a "police court judge" and a Klan member made it still more difficult for some people to accept the idea that he could be an educated man. But time and again, throughout history, intelligence and learning have appeared in unlikely individuals. The "American dream" rests on the irony that a person of humble origin without the initial advantages of family position and material wealth can yet reach the seats of the mighty. The American credo fancies the dream to be the norm, but when the dream in fact materializes it excites public interest as though it were the variant. Such a life as Hugo Black's often perplexes those who undertake to analyze it, while at the same time it rekindles public belief in the vitality of the dream. He was and is to many an enigmatic figure.[14] His reading interests, his reading habits, and his acquisitions of books simultaneously contribute to the enigma and to his fulfillment of the American dream.

The Setting

The books which Justice Black valued most were in his study at home, not in his chambers at the Supreme Court. Visitors who gained an audience with him at the Court—especially student groups—would often

[11] Note 6, *supra*.

[12] Hamilton, *Hugo Black: The Alabama Years* 46 (1972).

[13] Note 5, *supra* at 46.

[14] For insights into the enigma, see Durr, Hugo Black, Southerner: I. The Southern Background, 10 *Am. U. L. Rev.* 27 (1961).

run their eyes eagerly along his office shelves, hoping to gather insights into his reading interests and from that perhaps to deduce something about his ideas. But whatever they gathered was misleading. With few exceptions, and aside from legal works, the books in his chambers were apt to be unsolicited copies from publishers, or government publications, which were simply stuck on the shelves to get them out of the way. Black's intellectual life centered in his study in his Alexandria home where he read and worked much of the time at nights, on weekends, and on days the Court was not sitting. For law clerks and others who knew him well over the last three decades of his life, this interrelationship of mind and place and books is memorable.

The study was on the second floor of Black's house at 619 South Lee Street. In that area of old Alexandria, just before the land slopes down to the Potomac, eighteenth-century townhouses mingle with their twentieth-century imitations. Black's two-story brick house was built around 1790.[15] He acquired it in 1939, two years after he went on the Court. Flush with the sidewalk, in the style of its period, the house is set in a walled garden of over half an acre extending to its side and rear, affording an unusual amount of outdoor privacy in a tightly packed neighborhood. Within this house and garden, with a tennis court which he built, Justice Black created a largely self-sufficient world which changed relatively little for over thirty years. He was withdrawn from politics, and Washington social life had little appeal. Once on the Supreme Court, he entered essentially into a life of the mind, leavened with vigorous doses of tennis and gardening and by associations with family, law clerks, secretary, and fellow Justices. His messenger and his housekeeper, both native Alabamians of many years' service, rounded out the supporting cast.

The upstairs corner study was known well to Justice Black's law clerks. Much of the editing and discussing of opinion drafts went on there, sometimes long into the night. This was particularly so when he was living alone during the years between the death of his first wife in 1951 and his remarriage in 1957. Yet the room was more than a reading and work room. It was large enough—some eighteen feet square—to serve as a family room too. Against the front wall were a deep-cushioned sofa and a coffee table, flanked by comfortable chairs. In later years a television set was installed. After his remarriage he had a typewriter and small typing desk brought in for his wife, Elizabeth, so they could

[15] The house is pictured and described in Davis, Dorsey, & Hall, *Alexandria Houses, 1750–1830* 112–14 (1946); Moore, *Seaport in Virginia: George Washington's Alexandria* 222–24 (1949); *N.Y. Times*, Jan. 24, 1970, p. 19.

work or read in the same room, as they often did until well after midnight. Visitors and family members gathered there from time to time. Over the years the room was the scene of countless stimulating conversations. There the hour-long televised interview of Justice Black was filmed in 1967. The Justice's annual birthday gatherings flowed in and out. Bridge games at times droned away. At small, informal dinner parties guests sometimes assembled there.

For all this, though, the room most importantly was the place where Black himself read and reflected. The heart of his reading interests was in the books shelved within a few feet of where he worked at a library table which had come originally from the Supreme Court. Behind this table, often cluttered with books and papers, Black always sat in a leather swivel chair to read or to work on opinions. The window to the right of his chair faced south overlooking a portion of the garden, but the view was screened by a large magnolia tree. In later years, after the invention of the air conditioner, one was installed there. The shelves and cabinets immediately behind the table and chair contained working law books—the *Lawyers' Edition* of Supreme Court decisions, a digest to those reports, the *United States Code Annotated*, and a set of *American Jurisprudence*—in addition to a large number of other books. Along the wall to the Justice's left, opposite the fireplace, were non-legal works—the main body of his personal library—which make up much of the catalogue published here. Books filled seven shelves on that wall, running from the hall door to the front of the room. Four book wagons, each with two shelves, were filled with volumes. A small bookcase behind the door to the hall contained the *Encyclopaedia Britannica*. A globe stood on the work table.

Evidences of Black's career, along with pictures of selected heroes, adorned the walls of the study. There were sixteen group photographs of the Supreme Court, depicting its evolving membership from his first term to the last. Franklin D. Roosevelt was pictured addressing a joint session of Congress, with the Court sitting in the front row of the House chamber. The mirror over the mantel was bordered by engravings of Benjamin Franklin, Thomas Jefferson, John Marshall, and Andrew Jackson. The mantel held three small busts: Thomas Jefferson, Abraham Lincoln, and Franklin D. Roosevelt. Also on the mantel were the two Thomas Jefferson Award medals presented to Justice Black by the Southern Conference for Human Welfare and a medal commemorating the 1965 inauguration of President Lyndon Johnson. An engraving of the first Justice John Marshall Harlan hung nearby, along with another of Thomas Jefferson. On the front wall, between the windows, were photographs of George W. Norris, William O. Douglas, and Charles Evans Hughes. Louis D. Brandeis' picture was near the door into the hall.

In the far corner by the front wall of the room hung honorary doctorates from the University of Alabama (1935) and Auburn (1941). Also in that corner hung the order of the Clay County Court of June 4, 1906, admitting Hugo L. Black to the practice of Law in Alabama "at the age of twenty years, with disabilities of non-age removed." Immediately adjacent hung the form completed and signed in the handwriting of President Roosevelt: "I nominate Hugo L. Black of Alabama to be an Associate Justice of the Supreme Court of the United States." The juxtaposition of those two documents was perhaps not accidental. They symbolized a thirty-one year journey from the obscurity of the southern hill country to the pinnacle of national power—"a long journey," he said, "a fact which no one knows better than I."[16]

A plaster bas-relief of George Washington was by the window next to the work table and chair. In that same space was the only English picture in the room, a *Vanity Fair* print entitled "The Lord Chief Baron."

The photographs and mementos flowed out into the upstairs hall. There on all sides, and continuing down the stair wall which led to the main floor, were framed cartoons, photographs of public occasions, and snapshots with family and friends.

All in all the study was a pleasant room conducive to reading and thinking. When the wind was stirring, the rustling of the magnolia leaves just outside the window was faintly audible. But the thick walls of the house kept out most of the distracting noises of the twentieth century. In the later years, though, during winter months when the air conditioner was off, one could detect the sound of jet planes over the Potomac as they approached and departed Washington National Airport. Even so, the room with its walls of books remained intellectually inviting and peaceful. It evoked the image of a private library projected by Will Durant in the 1929 magazine article which Black had clipped then and kept all the years since:

If I were rich I would have many books. . . . I would have my library spacious and dark and cool, safe from alien sights and sounds, with slender casements opening on quiet fields, voluptuous chairs inviting communion and reverie, shaded lamps illuminating sanctuaries here and there, and every inch of the walls concealed with the mental heritage of our race. And there at any hour my hand or spirit would welcome my friends, if their souls were hungry and their hands were clean.[17]

[16] Black, *A Constitutional Faith* 65 (New York: Alfred A. Knopf, 1968).
[17] Note 3, *supra*.

Acquisitions

Most of Black's favorite books were probably acquired during his two
Senate terms and in his first few years on the Court, roughly from 1926
to the mid-nineteen forties. However, he continued buying books off
and on and receiving them as gifts during the rest of his life. In most
instances the date of his acquisition of a book cannot be precisely ascertained. A small number of volumes were in his possession before he went
to the Senate. Some belonged to his first wife, Josephine, or to her father,
Dr. Sterling Foster. The bulk of the collection, though, he acquired by
purchasing a volume or a set here and there, a little at a time. Many of
these were out of print and were bought second hand. They were often
editions of many years earlier. Some were quite old. His set of Livy, for
example, was published in 1814. Black intermittently scanned catalogues
from used book dealers to spot books he wanted. He was reported to
have been looking in London bookstores for volumes of Aristotle and
Thucydides when he was there in 1937 just before taking his seat on the
Court.[18] He did not often purchase newly published books. When he
bought books he did not usually write in the date, but books which came
to him as gifts frequently contained a personal, dated inscription. As to
books published during his lifetime, the publication date of course fixes
the earliest time at which the book could have come into his hands. But
as to most of the items listed in this catalogue there is no ready way to
tell just when he acquired them.

Black was not a book collector in the usual sense. He did not use his
shelves as a showcase. He had no interest, for example, in first editions
as distinguished from any other edition. He wanted only a readable edition. He had no desire to buy a book merely because it was rare or because it looked good on the shelf or because it made a good conversation
piece. He acquired a book solely for the purpose of reading it and of
having it thereafter on hand for reference or rereading. Bindings were
of concern to him only for their utilitarian function of protecting the
pages and holding them together. Few of his books had bindings of any
distinction or value; expensive bindings were more or less a happen-
stance. On the other hand, he was apparently not attracted to paper-
backs; he owned no more than a handful.

Black preferred to read and acquire the original writings of authors
in whose ideas he was interested, rather than books about their writings.
He wanted to see for himself what a person had to say; he was not

---

[18] Note 10, *supra* at 337–38.

satisfied with another's view of what an author meant. Since he read no foreign languages, however, he did rely on English translations of works which had been written originally in other languages.

This preference for original works influenced him in dealing with legal material. Thus he was not especially attracted to law review articles, though he did read them from time to time. Reprints arrived in his office continually. He would look with special interest at those written by former law clerks. And occasionally he would be moved to keep an article about the Court or himself or a Bill of Rights issue. Some sixty reprints were stuck here and there on his study shelves. But generally he thought of law review articles as merely another person's view of what courts had done. He preferred to read the full opinions themselves so that he could form his own judgment as to what they meant.

Black's reading habits and interests led him sometimes to read and acquire relatively obscure books. Even as to well known authors, he often thought their most significant writings were those which were lesser known or rarely ever mentioned. He had a way of ferreting out and becoming attached to out-of-the-way books or passages. He was a genuinely independent reader who cared little about what literary or historical critics said about a book, or about what was fashionable. He wanted to pursue his own interests, to read books for himself, and to do his own thinking about what he read.

Black also read many books which he did not own. As a Senator and a Supreme Court Justice he drew on the superb resources of the Library of Congress. From his chambers at the Court he could order by telephone from that Library almost any book ever printed and have it delivered in half an hour. In the main, though, the books on the shelves in his study included nearly all of those which in his mind were truly significant. They also included numerous volumes, accumulated in various ways, to which he attached comparatively little significance.

Reading and Marking

The significance of his books to Justice Black is best revealed, as far as tangible evidence goes, by his three-way system of markings, apparently devised at an early date. Markings included underlinings, marginal notations, and pencilled indexes. Black read carefully and thoughtfully. Typically he sat with pencil in hand, poised to underline passages—a few words or several lines—which struck him as either important or interesting. He would also jot an occasional notation of a word or so in the margin. In addition, he frequently constructed his own index inside the back or front covers. Marking the book in those three ways was, for him, an integral aspect of reading and assimilating.[19]

His underlining was an effort to identify the heart of what the author was trying to say. Underlining in itself did not necessarily reveal Black's view of the matter. It merely flagged the passage as one Black considered important to the text, or one which caught his interest for some reason. This should be kept in mind by anyone looking at his books. Black was just as apt to underline a statement with which he disagreed as he was a statement with which he agreed. The amount of underlining varied considerably from one book to another. Often he underlined copiously throughout an entire book, several passages on each page. Sometimes, though, he underlined only in a single chapter or on a few pages out of the entire volume. Most of the books which he liked were marked in some degree. Curiously, though, a few of his favorites contain little or no underlining, while a substantial amount of underlining appears in some books which exerted no special attraction.

Marginal notations were used by Black almost as often as underlining. These were typically of a neutral quality and were merely indicative of the idea or event being dealt with at that point in the text. In effect, he created his own key word index in the margins. As a rule, the marginal notations, like the underlinings, do not reveal agreement or disagreement; they do not editorialize on the text. Occasionally, though, they make a comparison, such as the notations "Like FDR," and "Like Pearl Harbor," which he wrote in Livy's history of Rome.[20] The meticulous nature of the marginal notes is impressive. They appear not only alongside the text but also in footnotes. Sometimes Black would even note in the text a case citation from a footnote located elsewhere in the book.

Black departed from the generally objective quality of the marginal notations in a few books dealing with the Supreme Court in his time, particularly where a book dealt with his own role. Examples are in Bickel's *The Least Dangerous Branch* and Mendelson's *Justices Black and Frankfurter: Conflict in the Court.* His disagreements there are clear. At numerous points in the margins of the Mendelson book Black wrote "untrue." In the Bickel book he made unusually lengthy marginal notes. For example, at one point he scribbled, "An implication, one of many, that my expressions of view about the First Amendment are intellectually dishonest." In books of this type, where he was directly involved, Black appears to have had an urge to set the record straight then and there, as though he were communicating with some unseen audience.

[19] In the alphabetical catalogue the words "marked" and "heavily marked" are used to include both underlinings and marginal notations. The words "personally indexed" refer to the pencil indexing inside the back and front covers.

[20] Livy, *The History of Rome*, Vol. 1, p. 475; Vol. 5, p. 70 (Baker tr. 1814).

A book of quite a different sort which moved Black to depart from his neutral style of marginal notations was Charles Reich's *The Greening of America*. Published near the end of his life, the book was one which he approached with a great deal of interest, since Reich was a former law clerk. Though he was personally fond of the author, Black was obviously at odds with numerous conclusions in the book. When, for example, Reich spoke of the destruction of the American dream, Black wrote: "I do not agree. It is not yet destroyed." And when Reich described what he saw to be the narrowing effects of law school, Black wrote: "Not necessarily at all." While reading the book Black let it be known to his clerks that he was a "Consciousness I" man. And when he finished, he announced with apparent relief that Charlie Reich did not believe in violent revolution.

Both the notations and the underlinings show an interest in human achievements and in human traits, good and bad, such as greed, trickery, flattery, and integrity. They show also a distinct interest in the ages at which people did things. For example, he underlined a statement by Thomas Jefferson that "at the age of seventy-six, I am again a hard student."[21] Sometimes he jotted in the margin the age of a person at the time of an event reported in the text. He often wrote in the date of an event if it did not clearly appear. He made quite a point of exact times and distances. In writings by or about judges he often flagged comments on problems peculiar to judicial life.

Indexing was the third feature of Black's marking system. He often pencilled his own index inside the front and back covers. Each entry consisted of a key word or phrase, with the page number. For example, "Virgil's Song 408," written inside the back cover of one of the volumes of Tacitus, served as his key to locate the point where that could be found. He usually began making entries inside the back cover, moved to the back flyleaf, and, if he needed still more room, he went over to the inside of the front cover or the front flyleaf.

In such a personally constructed index Black entered the matters dealt with in the book which he considered most significant, or most worth remembering, or to which he might want to refer again. Such items included the trivial as well as the important. His own interest, whatever the reason for it, was the controlling factor. His indexing varied in length from a single entry in the back of some books up to the entire back and front inside covers and flyleaves of others.

Most of Black's favorite books contain all three types of markings—underlined passages, marginal notations, and his personal index—all done by him in pencil. These evidence an unusually careful, critical reading.

[21] Malone, *Jefferson the Virginian* 55 (1948).

The likely effect of such a marking process was to imbed the contents of a book more firmly in his mind and to make the book an integral part of him. And the book was left with his own impress, making it easier for him to pick it up again and get to the heart of its ideas or to find the parts which interested him.

Favorite Literature

The books in Justice Black's collection are classified by subject in the listings which follow the alphabetical catalogue. Those listings reveal in broad outline the major areas of his interests. The comments here are designed to highlight more specifically the categories and the individual books of special importance to him.

High on Black's mental list of favorites were writings from ancient Greece and Rome and books about those civilizations. The attachment of Black to his copies of Thucydides, Plutarch, Tacitus, and Livy is legendary among his law clerks. These books occupied prime space on the shelves of his study. All were copiously underlined, annotated, and indexed in the typical Black fashion. To these and other books from Greece and Rome he often returned. *Plutarch's Lives* in his set of the *Harvard Classics* was as well marked as his separate edition of that work, thus showing at least two careful, complete readings. Actually, Black reread all or portions of his favorite books a number of times through the years.

Greece loomed larger in his mind than Rome. Something about the Greek culture in its golden age had taken permanent hold on his imagination. He traced this to his student days at the University of Alabama. "Since that time," he wrote years later, "I have had an ever-increasing interest in the literature, philosophy, and history of ancient Greece and the Greek way of life."[22] The problems the Greeks confronted, the ideas discussed in their literature, and the way they lived had, for him, a timeless relevance to human affairs.

If there is any single book out of the hundreds he owned which might be said to have been *the* favorite, it is Edith Hamilton's *The Greek Way*. This book held an extraordinary grip on his mind. He read it from cover to cover several times and seemed to know it almost from memory. Law clerks over a span of many years recall having *The Greek Way* recommended by Black in their initial interview with him, or in the early days of the clerkship.

Much of Justice Black's personality and views can be seen in this one

[22] Note 8, *supra* at 7.

book. For example, a chapter on the Greek way of writing is a good description of his own notions about writing style. One of the many underlined passages is this: "Clarity and simplicity of statement, the watchwords of the thinker, were the Greek poets' watchwords too."[23] No pair of words sums up Black's conception of good opinion writing more than "clarity and simplicity." His belief in the unchanging character of human nature also runs through this book. In the chapter on Thucydides, one of his favorite Greeks, an underlined passage captures one of Black's central beliefs: "He reasoned that since the nature of the human mind does not change any more than the nature of the human body, circumstances swayed by human nature are bound to repeat themselves, and in the same situation men are bound to act in the same way unless it is shown to them that such a course in other days ended disastrously."[24] More than any other single book, *The Greek Way* is essential reading for anyone attempting to understand the mind of Justice Black.

In the literature of both Greece and Rome Black thought there were important practical lessons to be learned about human affairs, in the present or in any other time. In that literature he found examples of despotic power and of the ways in which individual liberty had been maintained or lost which had their parallels in other eras, including his own. The writings of the Greeks and Romans were thus to him as relevant and applicable as those of the twentieth century. He saw them as a source of immediately useful wisdom and experience. He believed to an unusual degree in the universal and continued vitality of these classical writings, as his clerks can testify and as his markings in those books reveal.

Two examples can be cited. One is Plato's allegory of the cave in which men, watching shadows on the walls of a cave while chained with their backs to the outside light, believe the shadows to represent reality.[25] Black thought this was a superb description of the way people in our own time—and in all times—delude themselves as to reality and refuse to see people or events as they actually are. Another example is an incident which occurred shortly after Chief Justice Warren first came on the Court at the opening of the 1953 term. He sought advice from Black as to what he might read which would help him in writing judicial opinions. Black immediately recommended Aristotle's *Treatise on Rhetoric* as the best book on that subject.

Black's familiarity with Roman affairs, and his belief in their con-

---

[23] Hamilton, *The Greek Way* 75 (New York: W. W. Norton and Co., 1942).
[24] *Id.* at 184.
[25] Plato, *The Republic* 253 (Jowett tr. 1941).

temporary relevance, were exhibited during an unrehearsed public interview in which he cited Tacitus in connection with a discussion of obscenity and cited Augustus, Tiberius, and other Romans in some comments about overweening power of governors.[26] His way of relating ancient history to modern conditions was also illustrated in the course of an unpublished and little publicized tribute he delivered to Albert Einstein in New York City in 1955. He said:

About two thousand years ago Tacitus wrote the "Annals" of Rome. I wish many more Americans would read the "Annals" than do. The history was written, so Tacitus tells us, at one of those "times when men were blessed with the rare privilege of thinking with freedom and uttering what they thought." The degradation of individual liberty is graphically pictured from the time of the "beneficent" emperor Augustus to that of the cruel Nero. Tacitus tells about a first step taken by Augustus which undoubtedly seemed harmless to many, but eventually ended in a complete destruction of individual freedom. Under Rome's ancient law "actions were matters of trial but words were free." Only conduct could be punished as treason. Augustus did what James Madison long after referred to as giving a "new fangled" definition of treason. A man could thereafter be guilty of treason who merely criticized the emperor or the government. From this small beginning it finally became a commonplace to convict men for what they said or wrote. Even praise of politically unpopular men, or men the emperor did not like, became treason punishable by death. The property of "traitors" could go to the emperor or could go in whole or in part to spies or witnesses engaged in what Tacitus described as "the vile occupation of an informer." Tacitus described the times that followed in this way:

"At no time was the city in a state of deeper anxiety and alarm, never was there greater need of caution against a man's nearest relatives; men were afraid to meet, afraid to discourse: silence and distrust extended alike to strangers and acquaintances, and both were equally avoided: Even things dumb and inanimate, roofs and walls, were regarded with apprehension."

It was conditions like those Tacitus portrayed that caused Dr. Einstein to leave his native country forever and declare that he would not live in a land where thought and speech were not free.[27]

Here Black characteristically linked the times of Augustus and Madison and Hitler. The idea of recurring human themes constantly reappeared

---

[26] Cahn, Justice Black and First Amendment "Absolutes": A Public Interview, 37 *N.Y.U.L. Rev.* 549, 559–60 (1962). (This article is reprinted in its entirety in *One Man's Stand for Freedom* 467 [Dilliard ed., New York: Alfred A. Knopf, 1963].)

[27] Address by Mr. Justice Black, Einstein Memorial Meeting, Town Hall, New York, May 15, 1955 (privately printed) 3–4.

in his conversations, speeches, and opinions. In speaking of persecutions, he once remarked that there was nothing strange in what Hitler did. "It was simply a repetition of the course of history when people get too much power."[28]

The Einstein talk was given in the late days of the McCarthy era. Black had been deeply concerned during that time about the legality of the way aliens and alleged Communists were being officially treated. He was troubled about the free speech aspects of those cases and the use of anonymous informers, which he believed to be unconstitutional. There were several occasions when he summoned Roman authority to support his position. In his *Harvard Classics* he had come across a letter from Trajan to Pliny which he thought especially pertinent. In the letter Trajan had said, "Anonymous informations ought not to be received in any sort of prosecution. It is introducing a very dangerous precedent, and is quite foreign to the spirit of our age."[29] Black once commented that in all the history he had read Tiberius was about the only man of great prominence who had ever defended informers.[30]

When the Supreme Court refused habeas corpus to an enemy alien confined overseas by United States officials, Black wrote in dissent: "Conquest by the United States, unlike conquest by many other nations, does not mean tyranny. For our people, 'choose to maintain their greatness by justice rather than violence.'" In a footnote to that passage, he said: "This goal for government is not new. According to Tacitus, it was achieved by another people almost 2,000 years ago."[31]

In dissenting from affirmance of a conviction for refusing to answer questions before the House Un-American Activities Committee, one of Black's grounds was that the purpose of the Committee was to punish people because they had been Communists.[32] "The punishment imposed is generally punishment by humiliation and public shame," Black wrote. He invoked Plutarch in support of his view that "There is nothing strange or novel about this kind of punishment. It is in fact one of the oldest forms of governmental punishment known to mankind; branding, the pillory, ostracism, and subjection to public hatred being but a few examples of it."[33]

---

[28] *One Man's Stand for Freedom* 480 (Dilliard ed., New York: Alfred A. Knopf, 1963).

[29] 9 *Harvard Classics* 428 (New York: P. F. Collier and Son, 1909–10). He quoted this in his Carpentier Lectures at the Columbia Law School. Note 16, *supra* at 3.

[30] Note 26, *supra* at 560.

[31] Johnson v. Eisentrager, 339 U.S. 763, 798 n. 4 (1950) (dissenting opinion).

[32] Barenblatt v. United States, 360 U.S. 109, 134 (1959) (dissenting opinion).

[33] *Id.* at 153–54, citing, inter alia, IV *Plutarch's Lives* 43–44 (Clough, New Nat. ed. 1914).

In these ancient writings Black also found useful wisdom about ordinary human relations. In *Plutarch's Writings*, for example, he marked
numerous passages in an essay entitled, "How a Man May Receive
Advantage and Profit from His Enemies." In one such passage Diogenes
asked how to be revenged of an enemy: "The only way, says he, to gall
and fret him effectively is for yourself to appear a good and honest
man."[34] As in other books, these markings reflect Black's interest in the
theme of knowing oneself. For example:

Whenever then anything is spoken against you that is not true, do not pass
it by or despise it because it is false, but forthwith examine yourself, and
consider what you have said or done, what you have ever undertaken, or what
course you have ever had that may have given likelihood to the slander.[35]

Another of Plutarch's essays which he marked is "How to Know a
Flatterer from a Friend," a subject of no less concern to Black than to
anyone in high public office.

Reading aloud from favorite passages gave Black much pleasure.
Plato's account of the death of Socrates in the *Phaedo* was such a piece.
Once Black spent a large part of the evening reading it to a law clerk.

Ranking in importance in Black's mind with the literature of Greece
and Rome were the writings of Thomas Jefferson and other works from
the time of the formation of the Constitution, especially those dealing
with freedom of speech and religion. Few persons, if any, in the twentieth century have been more devoted to Jefferson's credo than Black.
To him, Jefferson's views on freedom of speech and religion had a powerful appeal. So completely did he embrace these and other ideas of
Jefferson that at the age of 84 he was called "an unreconstructed Jeffersonian."[36] Black probably read everything that Jefferson wrote which
survived in print. Here, as usual, he insisted on reading the original words
of the man himself.

The most heavily read and marked of Black's Jefferson books were
the four volumes of *Memoir, Correspondence, and Miscellanies* containing a wealth of Jefferson's own writings, edited by Thomas Jefferson
Randolph and published in 1829. Black treasured his copy of the small
book compiled by Jefferson himself entitled *The Life and Morals of
Jesus of Nazareth*.

[34] Plutarch, *Plutarch's Writings: Essays and Miscellaneous*, Vol. 1, p. 285 (Clough
and Goodwin eds., New York and Pittsburgh: Colonial Co., 1905).
[35] *Id.* at 291.
[36] Anthony Lewis, "The Authentic Voice," *N.Y. Times*, Oct. 5, 1970, p. 43,
col. 3.

In his major speeches as a Senator, Black commonly cited Jefferson[37] and in his opinions on the Court he continued to do so. The first occasion was in a patent case in his second term as a Justice; he dissented, relying in part on a statement made by Jefferson in 1790 as a member of the first Patent Board.[38] Perhaps Black's favorite Jeffersonian statement, and the one he quoted most often, came from the First Inaugural Address:

If there be any among us who would wish to dissolve this Union or to change its republican form, let them stand undisturbed as monuments of the safety with which error of opinion may be tolerated where reason is left free to combat it.[39]

Black invoked Jefferson most frequently in support of freedom of speech and of religion and related First Amendment issues.[40] But he relied on him in dealing with other issues also.[41]

Black enjoyed and owned books about Jefferson as well as Jefferson's own writings. He seems to have been particularly attracted to Claude G. Bowers' *Jefferson and Hamilton: The Struggle for Democracy in America*. A recent article suggests that this book contributed to Black's tendency in his Senate days to see issues in terms of a Jeffersonian-Hamiltonian dichotomy.[42] It is easy to believe that Black identified himself ideologically with Jefferson in the struggles portrayed there and that he saw the issues as still alive in his day. This book continued its influence; it cropped up at various times in Black's opinions long after he had left

[37] 72 *Cong. Rec.* 1500 (Jan. 13, 1930); 72 *Cong. Rec.* 5418 (March 17, 1930); 77 *Cong. Rec.* 1121 (April 3, 1933); I *Vital Speeches*, Social Security, 249, 251 (Jan. 14, 1935); 80 *Cong. Rec.* 4103 (March 20, 1936); III *Vital Speeches*, Reorganization of the Federal Judiciary, 674, 676 (Sept. 1, 1937).
[38] General Talking Pictures Corp. v. Western Elec. Co., 305 U.S. 124, 128 n. 1 (1938) (dissenting opinion).
[39] Quoted by Black in Konigsberg v. State Bar, 366 U.S. 36, 78 (1961) (dissenting opinion); Wilkinson v. United States, 365 U.S. 399, 422 n. 11 (1961) (dissenting opinion); American Communications Ass'n. v. Douds, 339 U.S. 382, 452 n. 11 (1950) (dissenting opinion); in his Carpentier Lectures at the Columbia Law School, note 16, *supra* at 49; in his James Madison Lecture at N.Y.U., The Bill of Rights, 35 *N.Y.U.L. Rev.* 865, 881 (1960), reprinted in *One Man's Stand for Freedom*, note 28, *supra* at 48; in his Einstein Memorial Address, note 27, *supra* at 5; and in his Swarthmore Commencement Address, June 6, 1955 (privately printed) 12.
[40] See Martin v. Struthers, 319 U.S. 141, 143 n. 3 (1943); Smith v. California, 361 U.S. 147, 157-58 n. 2 (1959); Communist Party v. Subversive Activities Control Board, 367 U.S. 1, 154-55 (1961) (dissenting opinion); Time, Inc. v. Hill, 385 U.S. 374, 400 n. 2 (1967) (concurring opinion); note 16, *supra* at 48.
[41] E.g., Hines v. Davidowitz, 312 U.S. 52, 63 n. 11 (1941) (federal-state sovereignty); Galloway v. United States, 319 U.S. 372, 397 n. 1 (1943) (jury trial).
[42] Haigh, Mr. Justice Black and the Written Constitution, 24 *Ala. L. Rev.* 15, 26 n. 79 (1971).

the Senate.[43] Bowers' *Jefferson in Power: The Death Struggle of the Federalists* was also heavily marked by Black.

Black was fond of the biography by Thomas E. Watson, *The Life and Times of Thomas Jefferson*. It contained one of his favorite literary passages, Watson's description of the friendship of Jefferson and Dabney Carr. Many times he read aloud that story of their youthful dreams and their hope of one day being buried together under the great oak tree on the hill at Monticello where they often sat and talked.[44] He never read it, he said, without tears coming to his eyes. Watson had both a viewpoint and a gift of language which appealed strongly to Black. Though a long generation apart, the two had much in common. Both were imbued with the attitudes of late nineteenth-century Southern populism, both liked the beauty of simple language, and both were ardent admirers of Thomas Jefferson. It is not surprising that the story of Jefferson told from Watson's perspective captivated Black.

Black owned the first two volumes of Dumas Malone's biographical work on Jefferson, and he had read and marked them.[45] But he did not have the sentimental attachment to that splendid scholarly treatment which he had to Watson's book. Also in Black's collection was a two-volume work, *Memoirs of the Honorable Thomas Jefferson*, done in 1809, of which only twenty sets reportedly were ever bound; apparently the printer became fearful of action against him under the libel laws.[46]

Among Black's other favorites from that period in American history were *The Federalist* and the writings of James Madison. One of his prized possessions was Saul Padover's *To Secure These Blessings*, a full account of the debates in the Constitutional Convention of 1787 arranged topically rather than chronologically. In the spring of 1971, a few months before his death, he gave his heavily marked copy to his grandson as a high school graduation present. The author promptly supplied Black with a fresh copy.

A little-known book written in 1927 by Leon Whipple, entitled *Our Ancient Liberties*, would be high on Black's list of favorites. This slim volume told in simple narrative form of the origin and development of

---

[43] Ludecke v. Watkins, 335 U.S. 160, 183 n. 7 (1948) (dissenting opinion); American Communications Ass'n. v. Douds, 339 U.S. 382, 453 n. 12 (1950) (dissenting opinion); Konigsberg v. State Bar, 366 U.S. 36, 66 n. 23 (1961) (dissenting opinion); Communist Party v. Subversive Activities Control Board, 367 U.S. 1, 155 n. 40 (1961) (dissenting opinion). In these opinions the book was cited for its description of the operation of the Alien and Sedition Acts.

[44] Watson, *The Life and Times of Thomas Jefferson* 23–26 (1903).

[45] Malone, *Jefferson the Virginian* (1948), and Malone, *Jefferson and The Rights of Man* (1951).

[46] Carpenter, *Memoirs of the Honorable Thomas Jefferson* (1809).

the key protections in the Bill of Rights, from their English roots to their absorption into American law. This was one of those books some-times put into a law clerk's hands as part of his "required reading." It was one of those few Black favorites which were completely unmarked. It appears to have been cited by Black in only one Supreme Court opinion,[47] thereby illustrating that the significance of a book to Black cannot be measured by how much or how little it was expressly mentioned in his opinions or speeches. This book is also an example of Black's ad-miration for certain little-known books.

Despite Black's attraction to American history, he seemed to have little interest in what George Washington had to say, just as he appar-ently paid little attention to Lincoln. The presence of a Lincoln bust on Black's mantel seems odd; it was probably a gift. In his historical uni-verse, Jefferson and Madison towered over all other American figures.

Along with the subjects of Greece, Rome, Thomas Jefferson, and the formative period of the American Constitution, Black would probably have ranked English constitutional history from the beginning of the seventeenth century to the time of the American Revolution. He liked to read about the English struggles for the protection of liberty against arbitrary governmental power. He was fascinated by the seventeenth century controversies over freedom of speech, press, and unorthodox beliefs. Macaulay's *The History of England From the Accession of James II* was a favorite. Once in a concurring opinion Black attached as an appendix a four-page excerpt from Macaulay's *History* to illustrate religious persecution.[48] In another case, in writing for the Court that there was no constitutional authority to try by court martial an honor-ably discharged airman, Black relied on Macaulay to show that standing armies and courts martial were relatively recent institutions.[49] In a 1935 Senate speech against an anti-lynching bill—a national issue at that time —Black developed an interesting argument from Macaulay's account of the way the Normans, after coming to England, tried unsuccessfully to deal with homicides committed against Normans by native Englishmen.[50] Black also liked the three volumes of Macaulay's *Critical and Historical Essays*. He had heavily marked the essays on Machiavelli and the Earl of Chatham (William Pitt). He was attracted to the high constitutional drama of Catherine Drinker Bowen's *The Lion and the Throne*. And he thought well of Lloyd Paul Stryker's biography of Thomas Erskine,

---

[47] Engel v. Vitale, 370 U.S. 421, 427 n. 9 (1962).

[48] Joint Anti-Fascist Refugee Committee v. McGrath, 341 U.S. 123, 146–49 (1951) (concurring opinion). Black also cited Macaulay in Everson v. Board of Education, 330 U.S. 1, 9 n. 5 (1947).

[49] Toth v. Quarles, 350 U.S. 11, 22 n. 21 (1955).

[50] 79 *Cong. Rec.* 6532 (April 29, 1935). Another of his references to Macaulay appears at 80 *Cong. Rec.* 3329 (March 5, 1936).

For the Defense. This was a book he occasionally recommended to his law clerks. It is cited in an opinion for an account of the *Dean of St. Asaph's Case,* one of those historical incidents which always excited Black, where as he put it, "jurors—plain people—have manfully stood up in defense of liberty against the importunities of judges and despite prevailing hysteria and prejudices."[51]

That case and numerous other English cases of similar vintage which Black cited through the years were reported in *Howell's State Trials.* Though Black did not own this set of books he drew on it often. Another work he often cited but did not own was Blackstone's *Commentaries.* His discovery of St. George Tucker's 1803 edition must have been a happy experience. For there he had Blackstone in an American package with accompanying commentary done in an unqualifiedly Jeffersonian spirit.[52] That he never acquired a copy is surprising. It probably never turned up in any of the second-hand and rare book catalogues which he perused occasionally.

John Lilburne and the Levellers were greatly admired by Black for their roles in the English struggles for liberty in the seventeenth century. He regarded the Levellers as the first real constitutionalists. He thought that they had come closer than any other movement to establishing a written constitution prior to the American federal and state constitutions. He acquired a book published in 1955, entitled *The Levellers,* which comprehensively treated that movement. In Black's hands it became heavily marked. The opening lines suggest why he found the book appealing:

The Levellers of seventeenth-century England faced, and faced up to, many of the social problems which are today plaguing the Western world. Such current issues in the United States as the propriety of loyalty oaths or the need to limit the scope of legislative investigating committees were issues which three hundred years ago helped to determine both the aims and techniques of the Leveller party. Indeed, the words of the chief Leveller spokesmen are often echoed with startling accuracy on the more progressive editorial pages of the 1950's.[53]

Another book on the subject with which he was thoroughly familiar, though he did not own a copy, was *The Leveller Tracts 1647–1652,* a

[51] Note 49, *supra* at 18–19.

[52] Black commented on Tucker's edition of Blackstone during the interview by Prof. Edmund Cahn, note 26, *supra* at 557. The explanation for Black's admiration for Tucker's work can be surmised from a recent review of a reprint of the entire set. Cover, Book Review, 70 *Colum. L. Rev.* 1475 (1970).

[53] Frank, *The Levellers: A History of the Writings of Three Seventeenth-Century Social Democrats—John Lilburne, Richard Overton, William Walwyn* 1 (Cambridge, Mass.: Harvard University Press, 1955).

collection of the major writings from that movement.[54] He cited both of these books and other Leveller sources from time to time.[55]

The Pilgrim's Progress was included in Black's volume of John Bunyan's writings; it was also in his set of the *Harvard Classics*. While this probably could not be called a favorite book, Black did consider it significant. He said that his mother had read it to him as a child. While working on the Court's opinion in the public school prayer case[56] he read some in it and kept it available on his desk. It is referred to in that opinion as well as in other opinions he wrote.[57]

Although Black owned numerous books on English history and had a deep interest in that subject, he was not an Anglophile. He drew on the English experience, chiefly in the seventeenth and eighteenth centuries, for the lessons it taught about governments and people and for its utility in shedding light on current Bill of Rights issues. He thought English history was important also because it influenced the men who wrote the Constitution. He showed little concern for English history before the time of Coke and James I—except perhaps for Magna Carta—or after the American Revolution. Nor did he seem to be favorably impressed with the courts at Westminster. The ceremonial trappings of English justice meant nothing to him. His thinking in these respects, as in others, set him apart from many American lawyers and judges. He was interested, however, in Jeremy Bentham and owned three of his books.[58] Charles James Fox was among the Englishmen he admired; he owned a six-volume set of his speeches.

If Justice Black had been forced to choose a single set of books to keep while giving up all others, a good guess is that he might have chosen the *Harvard Classics*. In those fifty volumes, which occupied prime space on his study shelves, he found a gold mine of good reading. He often expressed admiration for the entire set. In 1956 he sought to locate another which he might purchase and give to a library then being established in his hometown of Ashland. Some of his favorite pieces in that

---

[54] *The Leveller Tracts, 1647–1653* (Haller and Davies eds. 1944).

[55] See note 16, *supra* at 4–6, 32; Black, The Bill of Rights, 35 *N.Y.U.L. Rev.* 865, 867–68 (1960), reprinted in *One Man's Stand for Freedom* 31, 34–35 (Dilliard ed. 1963); Goldberg v. Kelly, 397 U.S. 254, 273 n. 2 (1970) (dissenting opinion); In re Winship, 397 U.S. 358, 384 n. 12 (1970) (dissenting opinion).

[56] Note 47, *supra*. While working on that case he also spent time reading Pullan, *The History of the Book of Common Prayer* (1900), a book he apparently did not own.

[57] Note 47, *supra* at 433 n. 18; Uphaus v. Wyman, 364 U.S. 388, 399 (1960) (dissenting opinion); Communist Party v. Subversive Activities Control Board, 367 U.S. 1, 151 n. 31 (1961) (dissenting opinion).

[58] Black cited Bentham in In re Oliver, 333 U.S. 257, 269 n. 21 (1948); In re Groban, 352 U.S. 330, 341 n. 13 (1957) (dissenting opinion); Hawkins v. United States, 358 U.S. 74, 76 n. 4 (1958).

set of books, all marked in his unique way, include: Adam Smith, *An Inquiry into the Nature and Causes of the Wealth of Nations*;[59] John Stuart Mill, *Essay on Liberty* and *Autobiography*;[60] John Milton, *Areopagitica*;[61] Sidney Smith, *Fallacies of Anti-Reformers* (a review of Jeremy Bentham's *Book of Fallacies*).[62] And there are many other favorites scattered through these volumes. *Fallacies of Anti-Reformers* was one of those pieces from which he liked to read aloud occasionally, with mock solemnity and pompousness, tinged with mirth and punctuated with laughter. He thought it an excellent compilation of the opposition arguments apt to be encountered in any time and place when change is proposed.

The books and types of books mentioned up to this point were the core of Justice Black's personal favorites. There were of course many other books on the shelves of his study (and a few in his chambers at the Court) which he read and liked and found useful. These can be sorted into several categories: European history; American history, after the formative period of the Revolution and Constitution; American law; contemporary affairs; Alabama and the South; and reference works.

The aspect of European history which interested Black the most was the French Revolution. His interest may have been developed indirectly through Jefferson's admiration for that democratic movement. Books on the subject by two of his favorite authors appealed to him. He considered Thomas E. Watson's *The Story of France* to be a good one-volume history of that period. And he admired Claude Bowers' *Pierre Vergniaud: Voice of the French Revolution*. Black's view of the latter was reported by Bowers himself after having been seated by Black at a 1954 dinner in Washington. Bowers noted in his diary that "Justice Black, who is partial to my books on American political history, amazed me by praising my *Vergniaud* as a book all Americans should read."[63]

Black owned H. G. Wells' *The Outline of History* and read it probably at a relatively early date. He once assigned it to a law clerk. A thin volume brought out in 1968 by Will and Ariel Durant, entitled *The Lessons of History*, was read and extensively marked by Black.[64] He was impressed enough with the book to send a copy of it to Lyndon Johnson

[59] *Harvard Classics*, Vol. 10.
[60] *Id.*, Vol. 25.
[61] *Id.*, Vol. 3.
[62] *Id.*, Vol. 27, p. 237.
[63] Bowers, *My Life: The Memoirs of Claude Bowers* 324 (New York: Simon and Schuster, 1962).
[64] His reading of this book came at the time the Supreme Court had the *Louisiana Boundary Case* under consideration. In a dissenting opinion he quoted the Durants' graphic description of the flux of the sea and the land. U.S. v. Louisiana, 394 U.S. 11, 79 n. 4 (1969) (dissenting opinion).

when he left the Presidency in 1969. Johnson and Black had long been friends and mutual admirers. Their relationship seemed to become even closer during Johnson's years in the White House.

Among Black's books on American history and American law were a substantial number about the Supreme Court and its Justices. Warren's *The Supreme Court in United States History* and Beveridge's *The Life of John Marshall* were well marked. He was interested though in general history as much or more than what might be called legal history. He liked the works of Charles Beard. He owned George Bancroft's ten-volume history of the United States and had it rebound in leather in 1964, an unusual step for Black. This was one of the relatively few works of real interest to him which he kept at the Court and not at home. He had copiously marked passages in a two-volume work by Thomas Hart Benton entitled *Thirty Years' View*, which covered American political history from 1820 to 1850. He liked Draper's *History of the American Civil War*, in three volumes, and once passed it on to Justice Harlan. Black and Harlan were distant cousins, a little known relationship in which Black took considerable pride; the community where Black was born was named Harlan, and one of his hero Justices of the past was the first Justice Harlan.

Main Currents in American Thought, by Vernon Louis Parrington, interested Black. He recommended it to others over a period of years. Here, as in Bowers' *Jefferson and Hamilton*, ran the theme of the two competing economic and political views in American history, both still alive, so Black thought, in the twentieth century, each in a continual struggle for dominance. This book appealed to Black probably for two reasons. The first was that it dealt with the idea of the timelessness of issues. As Parrington put it in speaking of the colonial debates: "The subjects with which they dealt are old-fashioned only in manner and dress; at heart they were much the same themes with which we are engaged, and with which our children will be engaged after us."[65] The second was the point of view from which the book was written—"Jeffersonian rather than Federalistic," as the author acknowledged in his Foreword.[66]

Black was not especially interested in keeping up with the latest books coming off the presses, and he was largely unaffected by fads in reading. Over the years authors and publishers sent him complimentary copies of many new books concerning contemporary affairs. He would usually glance through them, but few took on significance in his eyes.

[65] Parrington, *Main Currents in American Thought* i (New York: Harcourt, Brace and Co., 1943).

[66] *Id*. Black cited this book in Engel v. Vitale, note 47, *supra* at 427 n. 9, 434 n. 20.

Most of these books are not included in the catalogue here. Yet books did come along from time to time dealing with affairs contemporaneous with Black's public career which he viewed as having value. He found books by Harold Laski interesting. There were ten of them on the shelves of his study, some of which were inscribed to him in the handwriting of the author. *The Danger of Being a Gentleman* was formally dedicated "To Hugo and Josephine Black;" they had become personally acquainted with Laski in the nineteen thirties. The title essay in that book particularly appealed to Black, and he recommended it to some of his clerks. Clipped inside this book as a lengthy handwritten letter from Laski giving a pessimistic view of the future of European affairs as they appeared to him in 1939 in the shadow of Hitler.

Hitler's *Mein Kampf* was a book which Black thought significant. He owned a copy, obviously well read, with the characteristic pencil markings. He mentioned this book from time to time to his secretary and clerks. He had another book entitled *What Mein Kampf Means to America*. Apparently Black thought *Mein Kampf* illustrated the potential for stifling individual liberty which is inherent in too much unchecked power. Hitler may have served Black as a convenient and dramatic example of the consequences of not adhering rigidly to the First Amendment protections and to certain procedural safeguards. Black in a dissenting opinion once quoted at length from a Hitler speech.[67] Hitler may be an explanation of why Black thought that the Second World War was the only necessary or justifiable war in our history. In general, Black had a strong distaste for wars; he showed no interest in military history though history was his favorite subject.

In the early nineteen fifties Black acquired and read a number of books dealing with contemporary issues of loyalty, national security, and the First Amendment. A "Free Speech Library" was presented to him by his law clerks in 1952 to mark the fifteenth anniversary of his appointment to the Court; this was a collection of forty-two books of that type.[68]

While books on contemporary topics were not a major reading interest, Black read the newspapers regularly. He had a lively interest in the ongoing affairs of government, though he withdrew from political involvement as completely as any Justice. He would frequently discuss editorials or current events with his clerks, usually by way of relating them to long-range, fundamental issues or to historical episodes drawn from his books. He kept no systematic file of newspaper clippings, but

[67] Jay v. Boyd, 351 U.S. 345, 369 n. 12 (1956) (dissenting opinion).
[68] Each volume included in this "Free Speech Library" contains a bookplate with that designation. These books are indicated in the catalogue by the code FSL.

from time to time he would cut something out of a newspaper and stick it in a book, usually, but not always, a book to which the clipping had some relation. These clippings dealt with a wide range of subjects, from serious national issues, to historical incidents, to ordinary human problems. Newspaper clippings often served incidentally as bookmarks, along with such various items as invitations, postcards, old letters, and torn pieces of Kleenex. A bookmark was whatever was at hand at the moment.

Another sizable category of books in Black's collection concerned Alabama and the South. He accumulated much of what one would expect to find on the shelves of a man who had practiced law for twenty years in Alabama and had served two terms as a Senator from that state. Many of these items were local histories or other local publications of limited interest. Other than the fact that he kept them, there is no indication that they had any significance to Black. Perhaps he retained them for sentimental reasons. Despite his being ostracized by Alabama for two decades or more, his Southerner's sense of identity with home was never lost.

Though sentimental in some ways, with an abiding concern for his home region, Black was not romantically enamored with the South's past. He had no deep interest in reading about the Confederacy; in general he did not admire its leaders. He considered the Civil War the most disastrous of all American wars. His interest in it was chiefly in terms of its devastating aftermath in the South. He was impressed with portrayals of that period in Fleming's *Civil War and Reconstruction in Alabama* and in Bowers' *The Tragic Era*, which he had stuffed with newspaper clippings about more recent Southern problems. He referred to *The Tragic Era* once in a Senate speech as "that magnificent book."[69]

The Alabamian he admired most was J. L. M. Curry, and he owned a copy of his biography.[70] He thought that Curry's work in education for both white and black between the Civil War and the turn of the century was the kind of enlightened, constructive effort which the South sorely needed—then and later. Black was the type of Southerner who probably would have been a "Unionist" before the Civil War and who would have spoken later for reconciliation. One of his many random bookmarks was stuck in Henry Grady's famous "New South Address."[71] Like Grady, Black borrowed Benjamin Hill's progressive

---

[69] 79 *Cong. Rec.* 6520 (April 29, 1935); see also *id.* at 6532.

[70] Alderman and Gordon, *J. L. M. Curry: A Biography* (1911). Black's admiration for Curry can be seen in one of his Senate speeches, 79 *Cong. Rec.* 6521 (April 29, 1935).

[71] Harris, *Life of Henry W. Grady, Including His Writings and Speeches* 83 (1890).

and reconciling theme, "There is a South of Union and Freedom", and used it for his University of Georgia Law School dedication address in 1967.[72]

Black found pleasure in what might be called folk literature from the South. A book that ranked among his favorites was Baldwin's *The Flush Times of Alabama and Mississippi*, a series of humorous, raucous stories about frontier life in the eighteen thirties. This was a slice of southern history with which Black seemed to identify. Perhaps these anecdotes reminded him of his boyhood experiences in the Alabama hill country. The Jacksonian wit about "plain people" (an often-used Black expression) had a natural appeal to him. Black sometimes read aloud from this book, laughing so hard that he could barely continue. At times he kept it near his desk at the Court; at other times it was on a shelf in his study. In *Folksongs of Alabama* his torn-paper bookmarks were inserted at a number of songs.

Among the reference works in Black's collection were two complete editions of the *Encyclopaedia Britannica*—the 11th edition, which he thought the best, and the 1968 edition. The *Dictionary of American Biography*—a twenty-two volume set—was presented to him by all his former law clerks in February, 1956, at his seventieth birthday party. He marked in it here and there—for example, in the sketches of Grover Cleveland, the first Justice Harlan, St. George Tucker, James Wilson, and a few others. A dictionary was also close at hand around Black's chair. He was careful about choice of language and precision of meaning.

The Bible was an important book in Black's life. He was reared in devout Baptist surroundings. His mother read the Bible to him as a child, and he himself read it later. While a lawyer in Birmingham, he taught a popular men's class every Sunday morning in the First Baptist Church. There is no doubt that Black knew the Bible well and was attracted to many of its ideas, episodes, and poetic passages. How regularly he read it during his time on the Court is not clear. He quoted verses in at least four Supreme Court opinions and two public addresses.[73] In responding to questions about Bill of Rights "absolutes," he once said: "I have an idea there are some absolutes. I do not think I am far in that respect from the Holy Scriptures."[74] At the Fifth Circuit Judicial Conference in

[72] Black, There Is a South of Union and Freedom, 2 *Ga. L. Rev.* 10 (1967).

[73] In re Summers, 325 U.S. 561, 575 n. 1 (1945) (dissenting opinion); Johnson v. Eisentrager, 339 U.S. 763, 798 (1950) (dissenting opinion); Griffin v. Illinois, 351 U.S. 12, 16 n. 10 (1956); In re Groban, 352 U.S. 330, 341 n. 13 (1957) (dissenting opinion); note 16, *supra* at 4; Swarthmore Commencement Address, June 6, 1955 (Privately printed) 10.

[74] Note 26, *supra* at 562.

1970 he surprised the audience by producing a Bible from a package wrapped in newspaper; he proceeded to read the Thirteenth Chapter of First Corinthians. This, he explained in his tone of facetious humor, was by way of answering those critics who claimed that he had forbidden the Bible to be read. It was a moving performance and one of his last public talks.

As is true of everyone, Black's reading interests had certain voids and thin spots. He cared little for modern fiction and read almost none. He did, though, read some fictional works from earlier times, such as those of Mark Twain and Charles Dickens. But the dearth of fiction in his library accurately reflected his general lack of interest in such writings. Similarly Black paid little attention to books dealing with art, music, drama, science, economics, or military history. He seemed relatively uninterested in the medieval period. Adventure stories apparently had no appeal for him. And though he participated in numerous decisions involving allegedly obscene literature, he owned no books of that type except *Ulysses*, and apparently that did not interest him.

Poetry was more fully represented among his books. But other than Shakespeare and writings from ancient Greece and Rome, poetry generally was not a major interest. However, he was fond of humorous ditties and patriotic and sentimental verses. He carried in his memory a mixed bag of these which he would recite or sing on various occasions, always with enthusiasm. Typical of verses he liked to repeat with barely suppressed laughter was this bit which he said he recalled from a toast made at his 1906 Law School graduation by the Governor of Alabama:[75]

> Here's to Woman:
> Oh, the gladness of her gladness when she's glad,
> And the sadness of her sadness when she's sad.
> But the gladness of her gladness, and the sadness of her sadness
> Is nothing to her madness when she's mad.

A small book called *Heart Throbs*, full of little-known doggerel, was a favorite. He mislaid it a few years before his death and sporadically searched for it, unsuccessfully. A sequel, entitled *More Heart Throbs*, apparently of lesser merit in his view, is listed in the catalogue. An example of a patriotic-sentimental poem which appealed to him, and which he recited from time to time, is this:

[75] Recited in his Swarthmore Commencement Address, June 6, 1955 (privately printed) 6.

> Here's to the gray of the wind swept north
> When we meet on the fields of France;
> May the spirit of Grant be with us there
> As the sons of the North advance.
>
> And here's to the blue of the sun-kissed sky,
> When we meet on the fields of France;
> May the spirit of Lee be with us there,
> As the sons of the South advance.
>
> But here's to the Blue and Gray as one
> When they meet on the fields of France;
> May the Spirit of God be with us all
> As the sons of the Flag advance.[76]

In his later years Black grew fond of the closing lines of "Thanatopsis." He quoted them during his nostalgic address to the Alabama State Bar in 1968, his first public appearance in the state for over a quarter-century. He thought those lines similar to what he called Virgil's Song, clearly one of his favorite passages. In tone and in substance Virgil's words seem to capture Justice Black's personality. Quite appropriately they were read at his funeral service in the National Cathedral:

Me, let the sacred muses lead to their soft retreats, their living fountains, and melodious groves, where I may dwell remote from care, master of myself, and under no necessity of doing every day what my heart condemns. Let me no more be seen at the wrangling bar, a pale and anxious candidate for precarious fame; and let neither the tumult of visitors crowding to my levee, nor the eager haste of officious freedmen disturb my morning rest. Let me live free from solitude, a stranger to the art of promising legacies, in order to buy the friendship of the great; and when nature shall give the signal to retire, may I possess no more than may be safely bequeathed to such friends as I shall think proper. At my funeral let no token of sorrow be seen, no pompous mockery of woe. Crown me with chaplets, strew flowers on my grave, and let my friends erect no vain memorial to tell where my remains are lodged.[77]

Judge and Company

Writing of the work of a Supreme Court Justice, Professor Paul Freund used Bentham's expression, "Judge and Company," meaning the judges

---

[76] Black, Address, 13 *Mo. B.J.* 173, 176 (1942).

[77] Tacitus, *The Works of Cornelius Tacitus*, Vol. 2, p. 408 (Murphy ed. 1813). The passage was marked by Justice Black.

and the advocates who interact to shape decisions.[78] In Justice Black's life on the Court, "Judge and Company" can be seen, in one light, as himself, his law clerks, and his books. Those elements all merged into the work on the cases and made a fascinating intellectual amalgam. The books were not an occasional diversion. Black read and reread continually. And he shared his reading interests and insights with his clerks, thereby enriching the educational value of the clerking experience. The process, for the clerk, began at the outset.

"Have you read these books?" This question from Justice Black was heard by many a new law clerk shortly after coming on the job. "These books" usually referred to some of his volumes of Tacitus, Thucydides, Plutarch, or Livy, or to *The Greek Way*, or to some other historical work he might happen to be reading at the moment. On getting a negative response, as he did all too often, Black would say something like: "Well, they're your first assignment. What they have to say about human nature and history is more relevant than anything I can think of to the issues now before the Court." Clerks came to see quickly that books such as these were an important part of the life of "the Judge," as they called him.

In the collective memory of the clerks, the Judge is seen popping through the door from his office into their room with an open book in his hand, one which he had been reading the night before, smiling over a passage describing an occurrence or a condition of long ago—it might have been fifty years or 2,000 years—which read as though it came out of the day's newspaper or the current advance sheets. He was always alert for items of that sort. In preparing for his commencement address at his daughter's Swarthmore graduation in 1955, he set his law clerks to searching headlines from newspapers published at the time of his own 1906 law school graduation; he selected and quoted several which could have been in a paper somewhere that very week. And in the same address he quoted statements with a contemporary ring made by Marcus Cato in 195 B.C.[79]

Almost every clerk can recall numerous small incidents in the day-to-day banter that went on in the Justice's chambers in which Black would draw a parallel between some current controversy and an event from history. "Well, of course this has been the problem since the time of Tacitus," he might say, with the added question, "you know that, don't you?" If the clerk acknowledged that he had not read Tacitus (or any of the several other works to which Black might similarly refer) he would be told quite emphatically by the Justice, "Well, you can't be

[78] Freund, *The Supreme Court of the United States* 145 (1961).
[79] Note 75, *supra* at 5.

a lawyer if you haven't." And the book, put into his hands by Black, would become assigned reading. When Black would tell a new law clerk to read *The Greek Way*, for example, in preparation for his work at the Court, he had in mind enhancing the clerk's general educational background with the hope ultimately of making him a better citizen. But he also thought of such reading as directly relevant to the problems presented by the Court's cases. He would rather have had his clerk spend his reading time on literature of that sort than on a book on federal jurisdiction. He seemed to think that his clerks had had enough technical indoctrination in law school.

Black had an interesting way of spontaneously mentioning ideas and historical incidents drawn from the literature which he had read. Yet there was no affectation about this. He did not flaunt his learning; he was not an intellectual exhibitionist. His written opinions reflected this, for though they often drew heavily on history, they presented the story in simple language so that "they"—his imaginary audience of ordinary people—could understand it. Likewise, his thorough knowledge of the classics did not generate in him any affection for Latin terms or long words of Latin derivation. Clerks were enjoined to avoid such and to use plain English.

The historical references in Black's conversations and opinions reflected not only the broad scope of his reading but also his sense of timelessness about human affairs. Reading was for him a means of instruction in human nature. He saw common threads in the actions and attitudes of people from the Greeks of Thucydides, through Jesus Christ, the Romans of Livy and Tacitus, England of the seventeenth century, the American struggle for independence and union, to the latest hour in the twentieth century. In the lives of men over a two thousand year spread of time and place he perceived repeated patterns of behavior —moments of glory and high purpose, acts of skulduggery, displays of the strengths and the weaknesses of character, persecutions of the weak by the powerful, triumph and disaster, corruption in public office, and struggles for liberty against arbitrary officialdom. He thought that the foibles of people and politics were essentially the same in all ages. With this sense of history and the human condition, there was for him little or nothing that was fundamentally new or different in the issues coming before the Supreme Court. Few judges have viewed ancient history, or even more recent history, as having such continuing relevance to current issues.

Though Black at times tended to exaggerate the virtues of the "little man" and the persecuted, he was too much of a realist and too well read in history to have believed that any individual or group was altogether free of human weaknesses or incapable of evil and wrongdoing. He sought throughout his public life to better the lot of humanity; he obviously believed that society could be improved through the actions of men and of government. Yet he could hardly have believed in the perfectibility of man. His experiences in life, in the rough and tumble of law practice and politics, together with his reading had apparently taught him that human nature was basically unchanging and that in all men there were simultaneously both good and evil.

While none who knew Justice Black could deny his familiarity with the great writings, there were those who thought he used them to buttress his own preconceived views. Whether he did this to a greater or lesser extent than other judges is difficult to assess. There is a tendency in everyone to look for what he wants to find. It is probably impossible to disentangle the effect on a mind of extensive reading over many years from the effect of external events and circumstances in the person's life. Ideas and information derived from Black's reading mingled with what he had seen and learned as a Clay County boy and later as a lawyer, politician, Senator, and Justice. The influence of his books cannot be measured merely by looking to the few express references in the Supreme Court opinions and public addresses cited here. Such citations may even be positively misleading, because the influence of his reading was so much more pervasive than this small collection of citations suggests.

The books from which that influence chiefly flowed are recorded in the catalogue which follows. Succeeding generations thereby can know something of what this Justice of the United States Supreme Court read and valued. Most of the books which he liked best, and which were of greatest significance to him, have been mentioned in this essay. But numerically they were only a small part of his total collection. And this essay is not comprehensive. In the catalogue there are dozens of other books from which he derived pleasure and benefit.

The books read by Justice Black, his unique reading habits and interests, and the ways in which he drew on his reading so vividly and immediately in his work as a judge all form an important part of his legacy. Judges, lawyers, public officials, students—indeed all citizens—can learn much from this aspect of his life. A lack of understanding of human nature in historic perspective may lead a society into inappropriate action when confronted with seemingly new problems and may give rise to uncertainties and lack of confidence which threaten its stability, and even its continued existence. Thus the timeliness of this literature will not diminish. For the judges of the future a realization of this is especially important. They will need to make such books part of their "company" if they, like the great judges of the past, are to contribute to the maintenance of a civilized legal order by applying the wisdom of the ages, in light of contemporary experience, to the just resolution of human conflict.

A Hugo Black Reading List

THIS list is intended as a succinct guide for exploring the central core of Justice Black's literary world. It prescribes essential reading for anyone desiring to become acquainted with the ideas and writings—in terms of both substance and style—which Justice Black valued most. Every book here was in his personal library. Each author, in the separate author list, published more than one work thought worthwhile by Black; and each of these authors was represented in Black's collection by more than one book.

Books

Aristotle	*Treatise on Rhetoric*
Baldwin	*The Flush Times of Alabama and Mississippi*
Bowers	*Jefferson and Hamilton: The Struggle for Democracy in America*
Frank	*The Levellers*
Hamilton	*The Greek Way*
Jefferson	*Memoir, Correspondence, and Miscellanies* (Randolph ed.)
Livy	*The History of Rome*
Macaulay	*Critical and Historical Essays*
Macaulay	*The History of England from the Accession of James II*
Milton	*Areopagitica*
Padover	*To Secure These Blessings*
Parrington	*Main Currents in American Thought*
Plutarch	*Essays*
Plutarch	*Lives*
Smith	*Fallacies of Anti-Reformers* (Harvard Classics, v. 27)
Tacitus	*The Works of Tacitus*
Thucydides	*The Peloponnesian War*
Watson	*The Life and Times of Thomas Jefferson*
Whipple	*Our Ancient Liberties*

Authors

Charles A. Beard	Harold J. Laski
Claude G. Bowers	John Stuart Mill
Edith Hamilton	Thomas E. Watson

Thomas Jefferson

Catalogue of
Mr. Justice Black's Books

Explanatory Key

Markings, Inscriptions, and Book Locations

IN THE catalogue which follows, each book is listed alphabetically by author, or by editor if there is an editor but no author. Edited works of multiple authorship are listed under the name of the editor. Compilations are listed under the name of the compiler. Works translated into English from other languages are shown under the name of the author, not the translator, unless the author is unknown and the translator contributed more than the mere translation—e.g., a book, by an unknown author would be listed under the translator if he also edited or annotated it. Books written anonymously and with no editor are listed alphabetically by title.

In each entry the following information is given in this order: name of author or editor (Ed.), complete title, editor (if there is one and there is also an author), translator (Tr.), number of volumes, edition, series, place of publication, publisher, and date of publication. "n.p." indicates that the place of publication and the identity of the publisher were not given in the book itself and could not be discovered by independent research. "n.d." indicates the same about the date of publication. Information enclosed in brackets was not contained in the book but was ascertained by independent research.

Markings and Inscriptions

If the book was marked by Justice Black his three types of markings—underlinings, marginal notations, and indexes—are indicated by the following words:

marked—The book contains at least some underlined passages or marginal notations or both.

heavily marked—The book has extensive underlinings or marginal notations or both; markings usually appear throughout the volume.

personally indexed—The book contains Justice Black's handwritten indexing notes in the inside back or front covers or flyleaves. The extent of the indexing is not indicated.

If the book bears an inscription to Justice Black this is indicated by the word "inscribed," with the name of the inscriber and the date, or "n.d." if no date was included in the inscription. No indication is given as to the contents of the inscription.

The letters FSL mean "Free Speech Library," indicating that the book was one of the group of forty-two publications presented to Justice Black by his law clerks in October, 1952.

Book Locations

The symbol in the lower right corner of each entry shows the precise location of the book, as Justice Black left it. The books were located in four different rooms. Most were in his study in his house in Alexandria, but others were in two downstairs rooms in that house and in his office at the Supreme Court.[1]

The exact shelf location of books in his upstairs study in Alexandria (all of which, except strictly legal works, are included in the catalogue) is given through the use of a code keyed to the shelves. Diagrams of the study shelves are provided below to aid in identifying a book's position in the room.

Shelf Locations of Books in the Study

As the diagrams below show, there were eight vertical tiers of shelves in the study. In the location code these are identified by the initial letter A through I, to correspond with the tiers shown in the diagrams. The number which comes next in the location code indicates the shelf in that tier; the shelves in each tier are numbered from the top down. The last number in the code indicates the order in which the book was placed on the shelf, counting from left to right as one looks at the shelf. For example, G 3–10 means that the book was in tier G on the third shelf from the top and was the tenth book from the left end of that shelf.

Below tiers A, B, C, and D (the shelves behind Justice Black's work table and chair) there was a protruding counter top, at about desk

---

[1] In the summer of 1973, as this book was going to press, Justice Black's house was sold by his estate. Most of the books catalogued here were placed on permanent deposit in the Library of the United States Supreme Court. A few, along with uncatalogued law books and some pieces of furniture from the study, were given to the University of Alabama Law School.

	A	B	C	D
	1	1	1	1
	2	2	2	2
Shelves	3	3	3	3
	4	4	4	4
	5	5	5	5
Counter top	LA	LB	LC	LD

Closed Cabinets	Law Books	CL B 1 / CL B 2 / CL B	Law Books	Law Books

Wall behind table and chair in Justice Black's study

	F		G	H	I
1			1	1	1
2			2	2	2
3			3	3	3
4			4	4	4
5			5	5	5
6			6	6	6
7		8	7	7	7

Shelves on the wall opposite the fireplace in Justice Black's study

height, on which many books were placed. Below this there were enclosed cabinets. Books lying on the counter top are designated by the prefix L. The next letter indicates the shelf tier above that part of the counter where the book was placed. Thus, L B indicates that the book was lying on the counter in front of shelf tier B. There was a flux in the books lying on the counter; some may have stayed there continuously, but others were taken from and returned to the shelves at various times. The locations coded here show the books more or less where Justice Black left them.

With the exception of the cabinet below tier B, the cabinets below the counter were filled with law books which are not included in the catalogue. Books in the cabinet shelves below tier B are included, however, with the code shown in the above diagram.

A small bookcase occupied entirely by the *Encyclopaedia Britannica* stood between tier D and the hall door. This is indicated in the code as E.

In the study there were four book wagons, or stands, of two shelves each. These are designated as w 1, w 2, w 3, and w 4. w 1 was to the left of the fireplace. The other three were on the right side of the fireplace along the wall under the window by the work table. w 4 was the closest to Justice Black's chair. The location of a book on the wagon is shown by the final number in the code, arrived at by counting from the left end of the top shelf and continuing through the second shelf, from left to right. For example, w 2–26 means that the book was in the wagon designated w 2 (just next to the fireplace) and was the twenty-sixth book from the left end of the top shelf. Whether the book was on the top shelf or the lower shelf is not expressly indicated.

Locations of Books Elsewhere in the Alexandria House

Books were kept in two other rooms in Justice Black's house. Both of these rooms were downstairs on the main floor and in the rear portion of the house. The "round room" opened to the rear of the main hallway. It was a small sitting room with several book shelves. Books located there are designated RR.

Behind the round room was a bedroom used for guests, referred to as the back bedroom. It also contained several book shelves, and books located there are designated BB.

In the main, books shelved in the round room and the back bedroom were of lesser interest to Justice Black than those in his study.

A few books are included in the catalogue without any location code. These books were in Justice Black's house, but no shelf location could be identified for them.

Books at the Supreme Court

Justice Black's chambers occupied three large, panelled rooms in the northeast corner of the Supreme Court Building. His own office was the corner room. It was flanked by his secretary's room and his law clerks' room. No books were kept in the former. Shelves in the latter were filled with law books, chiefly the *Federal Reporter*. The shelves in Justice Black's own room held the *United States Reports*, statutes, and miscellaneous other legal works. The remaining space was used for other kinds of books, many of which were mailed to him at the Court gratuitously by publishers and authors. From time to time, as the shelves overflowed, those books were weeded out. Books in which he had no interest were removed to a storage room elsewhere in the building; they are not included in the catalogue.

Books included in the catalogue which were in Justice Black's Supreme Court office are designated by the word "Court." Unlike the complete listing for the study, the listing here is selective; books are not included if they apparently had no significance to Justice Black.

Alphabetical Listing

[ABBOTT, JACOB]
Jonas, A Judge, or, Law Among the Boys.
  Boston: William D. Ticknor, 1840.   w 2–33

ABERNATHY, GLENN
The Right of Assembly and Association.
  Columbia: University of South Carolina Press, 1961.   I 2–3
  heavily marked, personally indexed.
  inscribed by the author, n.d.

ABERNETHY, THOMAS PERKINS
The Formative Period in Alabama, 1815–1828.
  Alabama State Department of Archives and History, Historical and
  Patriotic Series, No. 6. Montgomery: Brown Printing
  Co., 1922.   G 5–31
  marked.
  inscribed by J. E. Chappell, n.d.

ACTON, FIRST BARON [JOHN EMERICH EDWARD DALBERG-ACTON]
Essays on Freedom and Power.
  Glencoe, Ill.: Free Press, 2nd printing, 1949.   I 4–15
  heavily marked, personally indexed, FSL.

ADAMS, CHARLES FRANCIS
An Autobiography (1835–1915).
  Boston and New York: Houghton Mifflin Co., 1916.   w 3–8

ADAMS, HENRY
The Education of Henry Adams: An Autobiography.
  Boston and New York: Houghton Mifflin Co., 1918.   G 1–1

ADAMS, JAMES TRUSLOW
The Epic of America.
  Boston: Little, Brown and Co., 1931.   G 5–6
  heavily marked, personally indexed.

[ADAMS, JAMES TRUSLOW, *cont.*]
another copy.
   New York: Triangle Books, 1941.   I 2–7
   heavily marked.

The Living Jefferson.
   New York and London: Charles Scribner's Sons, 1936.   G 2–5

ADAMS, JOHN
A Defence of the Constitutions of Government of the United States of America.
   New York: H. Gaine, reprint, 1787.   G 2–16

Diary and Autobiography of John Adams.
   Ed. L. H. Butterfield, 4 v., Series I of the Adams Papers. New York: Atheneum, 1964.   G 6–28
   marked, personally indexed.

ADAMS, JOHN QUINCY
Letters of John Quincy Adams to Edward Livingston.
   Stereotype edition. Boston: Young Men's Antimasonic Association for the Diffusion of Truth, 1833.   G 2–11

ADDISON, JOSEPH
The Spectator.
   2 v. Philadelphia: J. B. Lippincott and Co., 1853.   G 1–17

AESCHYLUS
Aeschylus' Prometheus Bound and the Seven Against Thebes.
   Tr. Theodore Alois Buckley. Philadelphia: David McKay, 1897.   G 3–13

AESOP
Aesop's Fables.
   New York: Grosset and Dunlap, n.d.   G 6–24

AIKEN, CONRAD, ed.
Twentieth-Century American Poetry.
   1st Modern Library edition. New York: Modern Library (Random House), 1944.   H 3–30

AIKEN, WILLIAM APPLETON and HENNING, BASIL D., eds.
Conflict in Stuart England: Essays in Honour of Wallace Notestein.
New York: New York University Press, 1960.   Court

ALABAMA HISTORICAL SOCIETY
Transactions.
   v. 2 (1897–98). Tuscaloosa: Alabama Historical
Society, 1898.   G 6–24

ALDERMAN, EDWIN ANDERSON and GORDON,
ARMISTEAD CHURCHILL
J. L. M. Curry: A Biography.
   New York: Macmillan Co., 1911.   G 5–18

ALLEN, FREDERIC STURGES
Synonyms and Antonyms.
   New York and London: Harper and Bros., [1920].   W 1–9

ALLEN, IVAN
Atlanta From the Ashes.
   Atlanta: Ruralist Press, 1928.   G 6–9
   inscribed by the author, n.d.

AMADEO, SANTOS P.
*Argentine Constitutional Law: The Judicial Function in the Mainte-
nance of the Federal System and the Preservation of Individual Rights.*
   New York: Columbia University Press, 1943.   H 7–5

AMERICAN BAR ASSOCIATION
The Prosecution Function and the Defense Function.
   [New York: Institute of Judicial Administration], 1970.   W 3–20
   inscribed by Warren E. Burger, n.d.

AMERICAN CIVIL LIBERTIES UNION
Secret Detention by the Chicago Police.
   Glencoe, Ill.: Free Press, 1959.   W 4–13

*Work Ahead in Hope: 39th Annual Report July 1, 1958 to June 30,
1959.*
   New York: American Civil Liberties Union, [1960?].   I 2–28

The American College Dictionary.
  Ed. Clarence L. Barnhart. New York and Toronto: Random House,
  1956.   LB
  inscribed by Elizabeth Black, Christmas, 1959.

AMES, FISHER
*Works of Fisher Ames: Compiled by a Number of His Friends to
Which are Prefixed Notices of His Life and Character.*
  Boston: T. B. Wait and Co., 1809.   G 2–17
  marked, personally indexed.

Analectic Magazine: May 1814.
  Philadelphia: M. Thomas, 1814.   F 5–23
  marked.

ANDREWS, ISRAEL WARD
Manual of the Constitution of the United States.
  Cincinnati and New York: Van Antwerp, Bragg and
  Co., 1874.   CL B–2
  marked.
  inscribed by Mabel Rhett Goode Coyle, n.d.

ANTIEAU, CHESTER JAMES; DOWNEY, ARTHUR T.;
ROBERTS, EDWARD C.; et al.
*Freedom From Federal Establishment: Formation and Early History of
the First Amendment Religion Clauses.*
  Milwaukee: Bruce Publishing Co., [1964].   Court

APPIAN
Appian's Roman History.
  Tr. Horace White. v. 4 of 4, Loeb Classical Library. London: William
  Heinemann; New York: Macmillan Co., 1912–13.   F 3–14

ARCAYA, PEDRO MANUEL
The Gomez Regime in Venezuela and Its Background.
  Washington, D.C. and [Baltimore: Sun Printing
  Co.], 1936.   1 5–35
  inscribed by the author, n.d.

ARGOSY BOOK STORE
Catalogue 505: Americana, From the Collection of Andrew Christian Zabriskie and Ilo Orleans, With Other Recent Acquisitions.
New York: Argosy Book Store, 1964.   G 6–26

ARISTOPHANES
The Comedies of Aristophanes.
Tr. William James Hickie. 2 v., Bohn's Classical Library. London: George Bell and Sons, 1886.   F 2–5
marked.
inscribed by Buddy Cleveland, August 8, 1953.

ARISTOTLE
Aristotle's Constitution of Athens and Related Texts.
Tr. Kurt VonFritz and Ernst Kapp. New York: Hafner Publishing Co., 1950.   W 2–44
marked, personally indexed.

Aristotle's History of Animals, in Ten Books.
Tr. Richard Cresswell. London: George Bell and Sons, 1902.   F 2–7

Metaphysics, Books X–XIV, With English Translation by Hugh Tredennick, and Oeconomica and Magna Moralia, With English Translation by G. Cyril Armstrong.
Loeb Classical Library. Cambridge, Mass.: Harvard University Press; London: William Heinemann, reprint, 1947.   F 2–18

Aristotle's Politics: A Treatise on Government.
Ed. John Lubbock, tr. William Ellis. Hundred Books. London: George Routledge and Sons, 1895.   W 2–23
heavily marked, personally indexed.

Aristotle's Treatise on Rhetoric, Literally Translated from the Greek, With an Analysis by Thomas Hobbes, and a Series of Questions. Also, the Poetic of Aristotle, Literally Translated . . . by Theodore Buckley.
New edition. London: Henry G. Bohn, 1853.   F 3–18
marked, personally indexed.

ARNOLD, BYRON, comp.
Folksongs of Alabama.
University, Ala.: University of Alabama Press, 1950.   H 6–12

ARNOLD, THURMAN WESLEY
Fair Fights and Foul: A Dissenting Lawyer's Life.
  1st edition. New York: Harcourt, Brace and
  World, 1965.   H 7–10
  marked, personally indexed.
  inscribed by the author, June 23, 1965.

The Folklore of Capitalism.
  New Haven: Yale University Press; London: Oxford University
  Press, H. Milford, 1937.   W 1–38
  inscribed by the author, n.d.

Selections from the Letters and Legal Papers of Thurman Arnold.
  Washington, D.C.: privately printed by Merkle Press Co. for Victor
  H. Kramer, 1961.   F 3–1

another copy.   W 1–34

The Symbols of Government.
  New Haven: Yale University Press, 1935.   W 1–31

ART STUDENTS' LEAGUE OF NEW YORK
73rd Regular Session: September 15, 1948 to May 27, 1949.
  [New York: Art Students' League, 1949].   I 6–23

Art and Understanding.
  v. 1 (November 1929–March 1930). Washington, D.C.: Phillips
  Memorial Gallery, [1929–30].   I 6–29

ASCH, SHOLEM
The Nazarene.
  Tr. Maurice Samuel. New York: G. P. Putnam's Sons, 1939.
  marked, personally indexed.

ASHMORE, HARRY S.
An Epitaph for Dixie.
  New York: W. W. Norton and Co., 1958.   I 6–13

ASPEN INSTITUTE FOR HUMANISTIC STUDIES
Aspen Executives' Program: First and Second Weeks' Readings.
  n.p., n.d.   I 6–15
  heavily marked.

AVERY, MARY JOHNSTON
She Heard with Her Heart: Life of Mrs. R. D. Johnston, Founder and Guiding Spirit of Alabama Boys' Industrial School.
   Birmingham: Press of Birmingham Publishing Co., 1944.   I 6–24

BACON, FRANCIS
Advancement of Learning, and Novum Organum.
   Revised edition, World's Great Classics. New York: Colonial Press, 1899.   F 4–8
   heavily marked.

The Works of Francis Bacon, . . . and Lord High Chancellor of England.
   10 v., new edition. London: printed for C. and J. Rivington, 1826.   D 1–1

BAKER, EDWARD DICKINSON
Masterpieces of E. D. Baker.
   Ed. Oscar T. Shuck. No. 1 of Series: Eloquence of the Far West. San Francisco: privately published, 1899.   H 5–5

BAKER, LIVA
Felix Frankfurter.
   New York: Coward McCann, 1969.   I 6–30

BAKER, TIMOTHY
The Normans: The Men Who Made the English-Speaking World.
   New York: Macmillian Co., [1966].   Court

BALDWIN, JOSEPH G.
The Flush Times of Alabama and Mississippi: A Series of Sketches.
   New York: D. Appleton and Co., 1853.   G 6–19

BANCROFT, GEORGE
History of the Formation of the Constitution of the United States of America.
   2 v. New York: D. Appleton and Co., 1882.   G 3–15
   heavily marked, personally indexed.

History of the United States of America.
   10 v. Cambridge, Mass.: Riverside Press, rebound, 1964.   Court

BARING-GOULD, S[ABINE]
The Tragedy of the Caesars.
   4th edition. London: Methuen and Co., 1897.

BARNARD, HARRY
Eagle Forgotten: The Life of John Peter Altgeld.
   New York: Duell, Sloan and Pearce, 1948.   Court
   inscribed by John Frank, n.d.

BARR, STRINGFELLOW
*The Will of Zeus: A History of Greece From the Origins of Hellenic
Culture to the Death of Alexander.*
   1st edition. Philadelphia: J. B. Lippincott Co., 1961.   F 5–9
   inscribed by Dick Howard and Clay Long, February 27, 1963.

BARRETT, EDWARD L., JR.
*The Tenney Committee: Legislative Investigation of Subversive Activi-
ties in California.*
   Ithaca: Cornell University Press, 1951.   I 3–5
   FSL.

BARRETT, WILLIAM
What is Existentialism?
   No. 2 of Partisan Review Series. New York: Partisan
   Review, 1947.   I 6–32

BARTH, ALAN
Government by Investigation.
   New York: Viking Press, 1955.   I 4–18
   marked, personally indexed.
Heritage of Liberty.
   St. Louis: Webster Division, McGraw Hill Book
   Co., [1965].   CL B 2–26
The Price of Liberty.
   New York: Viking Press, 1961.   W 2–10

BARTLETT, JOHN
Familiar Quotations.
   Ed. Christopher Morley. 11th edition, revised and enlarged. Boston:
   Little, Brown and Co., 1940.   I 2–1

BEARD, CHARLES A.
The Republic: Conversations on Fundamentals.
  1st edition. New York: Viking Press, 1943.   G 3–5
  marked.
  inscribed by the author, October 1943.

BEARD, CHARLES A. and MARY R.
America in Midpassage.
  2 v. New York: Macmillan Co., 1939.   G 3–6

The American Spirit.
  v. 4 of The Rise of American Civilization. New York: Macmillan Co.,
  1942.   G 3–4
  marked.
  inscribed by the authors, n.d.

A Basic History of the United States.
  New Home Library. Philadelphia: Blakiston Co., 1944.   G 3–13
  inscribed by Lorraine and John Frank, Christmas 1944.

The Rise of American Civilization.
  1 v. edition. New York: Macmillan Co., 1930.   F 5–15
  marked, personally indexed.

BELLAMY, EDWARD
Looking Backward 2000–1887.
  Boston and New York: Houghton Mifflin Co.; Cambridge, Mass.:
  Riverside Press, 1929.   I 4–26

BEMIS, SAMUEL FLAGG
John Quincy Adams and the Union.
  A Borzoi Book. New York: Alfred A. Knopf, 1956.   G 4–32

BENET, WILLIAM ROSE, ed.
The Reader's Encyclopedia.
  New York: Thomas Y. Crowell Co., 1948.   I 2–14

BENSON, E[DWARD] F[REDERIC]
The Life of Alcibiades, The Idol of Athens.
  New York: D. Appleton and Co., 1929.   F 3–19

BENTHAM, JEREMY
A Fragment on Government.
 London: Oxford University Press, H. Milford, [1931].   w 3–11
 heavily marked.

An Introduction to the Principles of Morals and Legislation.
 Oxford: Clarendon Press; London, New York, and Toronto: Henry
 Frowde, 1907.   w 4–17
 marked.

Theory of Legislation.
 Tr. R. Hildreth from the French of Etienne Dumont. v. 6 of The
 Paternoster Library. London: Kegan Paul, Trench, Trubner and Co.,
 1911.   w 4–19
 marked, personally indexed.
 inscribed by C. J. Durr, February 10, 1921.

BENTON, THOMAS H.
*Thirty Years' View, or, A History of the Working of the American
Government for Thirty Years From 1820–1850.*
 v. 1 of 2. New York and London: D. Appleton and Co., 1854.
 w 1–19
 marked, personally indexed.

Thirty Years in the United States Senate.
 v. 2 of above.   w 1–20
 heavily marked, personally indexed.

BERELSON, BERNARD and JANOWITZ, MORRIS, eds.
Reader in Public Opinion and Communication.
 Glencoe, Ill.: Free Press, [1950].   1 3–38
 FSL.

BERGSON, HENRI
An Introduction to Metaphysics.
 Tr. T. E. Hulme. Revised edition. New York and London: G. P.
 Putnam's Sons, 1912.   G 2–7
 marked.

BERMAN, DANIEL M.
In Congress Assembled.
 New York: Macmillan Co., 1964.   CL B–5
 inscribed by the author, April 17, 1964.

[BERMAN, DANIEL M., *cont.*]
The Measure Is Man: The Political Philosophy of Hugo L. Black.
n.p., n.d.   Court

BERNSTEIN, PHILIP S.
What the Jews Believe.
New York: Farrar, Straus and Young, 7th printing, 1952.   F 1–26
marked.

BETH, LOREN P.
Politics, the Constitution, and the Supreme Court.
Evanston, Ill.: Row, Peterson, [1962].   Court
heavily marked.

BEVERIDGE, ALBERT J.
The Life of John Marshall.
4 v. Boston and New York: Houghton Mifflin
Co., 1916–1919.   B 1–3

[Bibles]
The Holy Bible.
Red Letter edition. Philadelphia: John C. Winston Co., n.d.   LA

The New English Bible: New Testament.
Oxford: Oxford University Press and Cambridge: University Press,
1961.   H 5–3

The New Indexed Bible.
Revised and enlarged edition. Chicago: John A. Dickson Publishing
Co., 1913.   H 5–4
heavily marked.

BICKEL, ALEXANDER M.
The Least Dangerous Branch: The Supreme Court at the Bar of Politics.
Indianapolis: Bobbs-Merrill Co., 1962.   CL B–10
heavily marked, personally indexed.

BIDDLE, FRANCIS
Justice Holmes, Natural Law and the Supreme Court.
New York: Macmillan Co., 1961.   B 1–12

Mr. Justice Holmes.
New York: Charles Scribner's Sons, 1942.   H 3–12
marked.

BIGELOW, JOHN
The Life of Samuel J. Tilden.
  2 v. New York: Harper and Bros., 1895.
  v. 1.   G 4–18
  v. 2.   G 1–15

BINGHAM, JOHN ARMOR
Trial of the Conspirators for the Assassination of President Lincoln and Company.
  Washington, D.C.: U.S. Government Printing
  Office, 1865.   G 3–10

BINGHAM, LOIS A.
How to Look at Works of Art: The Search for Line.
  Washington, D.C.: National Gallery of Art, 1946.   I 6–33

BIRMINGHAM, STEPHEN
The Right People: A Portrait of the American Social Establishment.
  Boston and Toronto: Little, Brown and Co., 1968.   H 7–7

BISHOP, CORTLAND F.
History of Elections in the American Colonies.
  Ed. University Faculty of Political Science of Columbia College. v.
  3, no. 1. New York: Columbia College, 1893.   G 2–22

BLACK, CHARLES L., JR.
The Occasions of Justice.
  New York: Macmillan Co., 1963.   CL B 2–7
  marked.

The People and the Court.
  New York: Macmillan Co., 1960.   CL B 2–2
  marked, personally indexed.

BLACK, HUGO LAFAYETTE
A Constitutional Faith.
  1st edition. New York: Alfred A. Knopf, 1968.   W 3–7
  inscribed by the author to his wife, Elizabeth, Christmas 1968.

Crença na Constituição.
  Rio de Janiero and São Paulo: Forense, 1970.   W 3–5

another copy.   W 3–6

BLAKLEY, HUNTER B.
Religion in Shoes: Brother Bryan of Birmingham.
 Revised edition. Richmond, Va.: John Knox Press, 1953.   1 2–1 2
 inscribed by the author, n.d.

another copy.   Court
 inscribed by Thomas C. Bryan, October 1962.

BLANSHARD, PAUL
American Freedom and Catholic Power.
 Boston: Beacon Press, 1949.   RR
 marked, personally indexed.

God and Man in Washington.
 Boston: Beacon Press, 1960.   RR

Religion and the Schools.
 Boston: Beacon Press, 1963.   1 5–28

BLOCK, HERBERT
The Herblock Gallery.
 New York: Simon and Schuster, 1968.   W 1–25

BLUNT, WILFRED
Cockerell: A Life of Sydney Carlyle Cockerell (1867–1962).
 A Borzoi Book. New York: Alfred A. Knopf, 1865.   Court

BONE, ROBERT G.
Ancient History With Questions and Answers.
 Ames, Iowa: Littlefield, Adams and Co., 1955.   W 1–32

BONNER, CLINT
How They Got There.
 n.p., n.d.   W 3–17

BONNER, ROBERT J.
Lawyers and Litigants in Ancient Athens: The Genesis of the Legal Profession.
 Chicago: University of Chicago Press, 1927.   F 5–21
 marked.

BONNER, ROBERT J. and SMITH, GERTRUDE
The Administration of Justice from Homer to Aristotle.
   v. 2. Chicago: University of Chicago Press, 1938.   F 5–2
   marked, personally indexed.

BONTECOU, ELEANOR
The Federal Loyalty-Security Program.
   1st edition. Ithaca: Cornell University Press, 1953.   I 4–6

BOORSTIN, DANIEL J.
The Lost World of Thomas Jefferson.
   New York: Henry Holt and Co., 1948.   G 2–3

BORKIN, JOSEPH
The Corrupt Judge: An Inquiry into Bribery and Other High Crimes and Misdemeanors in Federal Courts.
   New York: Clarkson N. Potter, 1962.   Court

another copy.   Court

BOTKIN, BENJAMIN ALBERT, ed.
A Treasury of Southern Folklore: Stories, Ballads, Traditions and Folkways of the People of the South.
   New York: Crown Publishers, 1949.   H 5–8

BOWEN, CATHERINE DRINKER
John Adams and the American Revolution.
   Boston: Little, Brown and Co., 1950.   G 2–10

The Lion and the Throne: The Life and Times of Sir Edward Coke (1552–1634).
   An Atlantic Monthly Press Book. Boston and Toronto: Little, Brown and Co., 1956.   F 5–26
   heavily marked.

Miracle at Philadelphia: The Story of the Constitutional Convention, May to September 1787.
   An Atlantic Monthly Press Book. Boston: Little, Brown and Co., 1966.   CL B 2–20
   heavily marked, personally indexed.

BOWERS, CLAUDE G.
Jefferson and Hamilton: The Struggle for Democracy in America.
  Boston and New York: Houghton Mifflin Co., 1925. G 4–10
  marked, personally indexed.

Jefferson in Power: The Death Struggle of the Federalists.
  Boston: Houghton Mifflin Co., 1936. G 4–9
  heavily marked, personally indexed.

My Life: The Memoirs of Claude Bowers.
  New York: Simon and Schuster, 1962. W 4–26

Pierre Vergniaud: Voice of the French Revolution.
  New York: Macmillan Co., 1st printing, 1950. I 5–18
  heavily marked, personally indexed.

The Tragic Era: The Revolution After Lincoln.
  Cambridge, Mass.: Houghton Mifflin Co., 1929. G 5–17

another copy.
  Cambridge, Mass.: Literary Guild of America, 1929. G 4–24
  marked.

another copy.
  Cambridge, Mass.: Riverside Press, 1929. F 5–25
  marked.

BOYD, MINNIE CLARE
Alabama in the Fifties: A Social Study.
  New York: Columbia University Press, 1931. G 6–20

BRANDEIS, LOUIS DEMBITZ
Urban Reformer: 1870–1907.
  Eds. Melvin I. Urofsky and David W. Levy. v. 1 of Letters. Albany:
  State University of New York Press, 1971. Court

The Words of Justice Brandeis.
  Ed. Solomon Goldman. New York: Henry
  Schuman, 1953. H 3–1

BRANDON, LEROY D., comp.
Platforms of the Two Great Political Parties: 1932 to 1940.
  Washington, D.C.: U.S. Government Printing
  Office, 1940. Court

BRANNON, HENRY
A Treatise on the Rights and Privileges Guaranteed by the Fourteenth Amendment to the Constitution of the United States.
   Cincinnati: W. H. Anderson and Co., 1901.   CL B–4
   marked.

BRANNON, PETER A.
A Little Black Volume: The Story of Curiosity's Reward.
   Montgomery, Ala.: Paragon Press, 1930.   G 5–29
   inscribed by William H. Thomas, n.d.

BRANT, IRVING
The Bill of Rights: Its Origin and Meaning.
   Indianapolis: Bobbs-Merrill Co., 1965.   W 4–29

BRANTLEY, WILLIAM H.
Chief Justice Stone of Alabama.
   Birmingham: privately published by Birmingham Publishing Co., 1943.   G 5–21

BRECHT, ARNOLD
The Political Philosophy of Arnold Brecht.
   Ed. Morris D. Forkosch. New York: Exposition Press, 1954.   RR
   marked.

BRENNAN, WILLIAM J.
Proceedings in Honor of Mr. Justice Brennan.
   Occasional Pamphlet No. 9. Cambridge, Mass.: Harvard Law School, 1967.   CL B 2–22

BREWER, DAVID J., ed.
World's Best Orations.
   10 v. Chicago: Fred P. Kaiser Publishing Co., 1899.   RR
another copy.
   Revised edition. Chicago: Fred P. Kaiser Publishing Co., 1923.   11–5
   marked.

BREWER, WILLIS
Alabama: Her History, Resources, War Record, and Public Men, From 1540 to 1872.
  Montgomery: Barrett and Brown Printers, 1872.   G 4–21

BRIGHAM, JOHNSON
James Harlan.
  Ed. Benjamin F. Shambaugh. Iowa Biographical Series. Iowa City: State Historical Society of Iowa, 1913.   Court

BROGAN, D[ENIS] W[ILLIAM]
Politics and Law in the United States.
  Cambridge: University Press, 1941.   W 4–3
  marked.
  inscribed by D. W. Brogan, n.d.

BROOKS, AUBREY LEE
Walter Clark: Fighting Judge.
  Chapel Hill: University of North Carolina Press, 1944.   I 6–12
  heavily marked, personally indexed.

BROOKS, VAN WYCK
Literature in New England: The Flowering of New England, 1815–1865. New England: Indian Summer, 1865–1915.
  Garden City: Garden City Publishing Co., [1944].   RR
  marked, personally indexed.

The World of Washington Irving.
  Philadelphia: Blakiston Co., 1944.   I 2–4
  marked, personally indexed.
  inscribed by Sid [Davis], March 26, 1945.

BROWDER, EARL
Victory and After.
  New York: International Publishers, 1942.   I 3–36

BROWN, VIRGINIA POUNDS and NABERS, JANE PORTER, eds.
Mary Gordon Duffee's Sketches of Alabama: Being an Account of the Journey from Tuscaloosa to Blount Springs Through Jefferson County on the Old Stage Roads.
  1st edition. University: University of Alabama
  Press, 1970.   G 6–29
  inscribed by the editors, n.d.

BROWNING, ROBERT
The Complete Poetic and Dramatic Works of Robert Browning.
 Cambridge edition. Boston and New York: Houghton Mifflin Co.,
 1895.   G 1–3

Men and Women.
 rebound, n.d.   RR

The Ring and the Book.
 v. 7 of the Complete Works of Robert Browning. New York:
 Thomas Y. Crowell Co., 1898.   G 1–10

BRYCE, JAMES
The American Commonwealth.
 2 v., 3rd edition. New York and London: Macmillan and
 Co., 1896.   1 2–19
 marked, personally indexed.

BUCHANAN, LAMONT
The Story of Tennis.
 Toronto: Copp Clark Co., 1951.   W 1–3
 inscribed by Frances and Spike [Kelley], February 27, 1952.

BUCKLE, HENRY THOMAS
History of Civilization in England.
 2 v., 2nd London edition. New York: D. Appleton and
 Co., 1880.   F 1–13
 heavily marked, personally indexed.

BUDGE, J. DONALD
Budge on Tennis.
 New York: Prentice Hall, 1939.   W 1–1
 marked.

BUDGE, LLOYD
Tennis Made Easy.
 New York: A. S. Barnes and Co., [1945].   W 1–5
 marked.

BULFINCH, THOMAS
The Age of Fable or Beauties of Mythology.
 Ed. J. Loughran Scott. Philadelphia: David McKay
 Publishers, 1898.   BB

[BULFINCH, THOMAS, *cont.*]
Bulfinch's Mythology: The Age of Fable, The Age of Chivalry, Legends of Charlemagne.
 Modern Library "Giant" Series. New York: Modern Library (Random House), [195–?].   F 4–11

BUNYAN, JOHN
The Complete Works of John Bunyan.
 Illustrated edition. Philadelphia: Bradley Garretson and Co.; Galesburg, Ill.; Columbus, Ohio; Nashville; and Houston: William Garretson and Co., 1872.   RR

BURTON, HAROLD H.
Memorial Publication of the Bar and Officers of the Supreme Court of the United States: Harold Hitz Burton. May 24, 1965.
 n.p.   H 3–45

The Occasional Papers of Mr. Justice Burton.
 Ed. Edward G. Hudon. Brunswick, Me.: Bowdoin
 College, 1969.   H 3–31
 inscribed by Selma Burton, May 19, 1969.

BURY, JOHN BAGNELL
A History of Freedom of Thought.
 2nd edition. London and New York: Oxford University
 Press, 1952.   W 2–46

A History of Greece to the Death of Alexander the Great.
 London: Macmillan Co., reprint of 2nd
 edition 1913, 1924.   F 2–14
 personally indexed.

BUSCH, NOEL F.
Adlai E. Stevenson of Illinois.
 New York: Farrar, Straus and Young, 1952.   I 2–9
 inscribed by Cooper Green, September 2, 1953.

BUTLER, CHARLES HENRY
A Century at the Bar of the Supreme Court of the United States.
 New York: G. P. Putnam's Sons, [1942].   Court
 inscribed by Henry T. Butler, December 25, 1941.

BUTLER, PIERCE
Proceedings in the U.S. Supreme Court in Memory of Pierce Butler,
January 27, 1940.
    Washington, D.C.: U.S. Government Printing
    Office, 1940.   H 3–36

BUTTS, R. FREEMAN
The American Tradition in Religion and Education.
    Boston: Beacon Press, 1950.   I 4–20

BYARS, WILLIAM VINCENT, ed.
The Handbook of Oratory.
    St. Louis and Chicago: Fred P. Kaiser, 1901.   I 1–4
    marked.

CAHN, EDGAR S., ed.
Our Brother's Keeper: The Indian in White America.
    New York and Cleveland: distributed by World Publishing
    Co., 1969.   Court

CAHN, EDMOND
Confronting Injustice: The Edmond Cahn Reader.
    Ed. Lenore Cahn. Foreword by Hugo L. Black. Boston: Little,
    Brown and Co., 1966.   CL B 2–10

The Moral Decision.
    Bloomington: Indiana University Press, 1955.   W 1–16
    inscribed by the author, 1956.

The Predicament of Democratic Man.
    New York: Macmillan Co.; Ontario:
    Brett-Macmillan, 1961.   W 1–17
    inscribed by the author, 1961.

The Sense of Injustice: An Anthropocentric View of the Law.
    New York: New York University Press, 1949.   CL B–10
    marked, personally indexed.
    inscribed by Jim Frack [?], n.d.

CAHN, EDMOND, ed.
The Great Rights.
    New York: Macmillan Co., 1963.   W 3–4

another copy.   LC

CAIRNS, HUNTINGTON
Law and Its Premises.
    20th Annual Benjamin N. Cardozo Lecture delivered before the Bar
Association of City of New York, November 1, 1962.   w 3–16

CAIRNS, HUNTINGTON; TATE, ALLEN; and
VAN DOREN, MARK, eds.
Invitation to Learning.
    New York: New Home Library, 1942.   I 5–24

CALAMANDREI, PIERO
Eulogy of Judges.
    Trs. John Clarke Adams and C. Abbott Phillips, Jr. Princeton: Prince-
ton University Press, 1946.   w 2–36

CAMPBELL, LORD
Lives of the Lord Chancellors and Keepers of the Great Seal of England.
    Ed. John Allan Mallory. New edition. Boston: Estes and Lauriat,
1874–75.   H 6–2
    marked, personally indexed.

CAMPBELL, THOMAS MONROE
The Movable School Goes to the Negro Farmer.
    Tuskegee, Ala.: Tuskegee Institute Press, 1936.   G 6–11

CAMUS, ALBERT
Resistance, Rebellion, and Death.
    Tr. Justin O'Brien. 1st American edition. New York: Alfred A.
Knopf, 1961.   H 6–10
    marked, personally indexed.

CANBY, HENRY SEIDEL and OPDYCKE, JOHN BAKER
Handbook of English Usage.
    New York: Macmillan Co., 1946.   w 2–38

CARCOPINO, JÉRÔME
Cicero: The Secrets of His Correspondence.
    Tr. E. O. Lorimer. 2 v., 1st edition. London: Routledge and Kegan
Paul, 1951.   F 3–10
    marked, personally indexed.

CARDOZO, BENJAMIN N.
The Growth of the Law.
New Haven: Yale University Press, 5th printing, 1934.   H 3–2
heavily marked.

Law and Literature and Other Essays and Addresses.
New York: Harcourt, Brace and Co., 1931.   B 1–34
marked.

The Nature of the Judicial Process.
New Haven: Yale University Press, 1937.   B 1–35
heavily marked.

Proceedings in the U.S. Supreme Court in Memory of Benjamin Nathan Cardozo, November 26, 1938.
Washington, D.C., 1938.   H 3–37

CARLYLE, THOMAS
Critical and Miscellaneous Essays.
2 v., Carlyle's Complete Works. Boston: Aldine Book Publishing Co., 1869.
v. 1 marked, personally indexed.   W 2–47
v. 2   BB

Frederick the Great.
4 v., Carlyle's Complete Works. Boston: Aldine Book Publishing Co., 1869.   BB

Oliver Cromwell's Letters and Speeches.
v. 1 & 2 of 3, Carlyle's Complete Works. Boston: Aldine Book Publishing Co., 1869.
v. 1   BB
v. 2   H 6–5

CARMER, CARL
Stars Fell on Alabama.
New York: Blue Ribbon Books, 1934.   I 6–20
marked.

CARPENTER, EDWARD
England's Ideal and Other Papers on Social Subjects.
Revised edition. London: Swan Sonnenschein and Co.; New York: Charles Scribner's Sons, 1895.   G 1–18

[CARPENTER, STEPHEN C.]
Memoirs of the Honorable Thomas Jefferson . . . , Containing a Concise History of Those States, From the Acknowledgement of Their Independence With a View of the Rise and Progress of French Influence and French Principles in That Country.
> 2 v. [New York]: printed for the purchasers, 1809.   G 2–12
> v. 1 marked, personally indexed.

CARR, ROBERT K.
The House Committee on Un-American Activities, 1945–1950.
> 1st edition. Ithaca: Cornell University Press, 1952.   I 4–8

CARREL, ALEXIS
Man, The Unknown.
> 59th edition. New York: Halcyon House, 1938.   I 6–19
> marked.

CARTER, RICHARD
Breakthrough: The Saga of Jonas Salk.
> New York: Trident Press, 1966.   Court

Ceremonies Attending the Sesquicentennial of the Battle of Horseshoe Bend and Dedication of the Park Visitor Center, Friday, March 27, 1964, 2 p.m.
> n.p.   W 1–13
> inscribed by C. J. "Jack" Coley, July 9, 1966.

CHAFEE, ZECHARIAH, JR.
The Blessings of Liberty.
> Philadelphia and New York: J. B. Lippincott and
> Co., 1956.   I 3–34

Free Speech in the United States.
> Cambridge, Mass.: Harvard University Press, 1948.   I 3–23
> FSL.

Government and Mass Communications: A Report from the Commission on Freedom of the Press.
> 2 v. Chicago: University of Chicago Press, 1947.
> FSL.
> v. 1   I 4–30
> v. 2   I 3–9

Three Human Rights in the Constitution of 1787.
> Lawrence: University of Kansas Press, 1956.   CL B 2–18

CHAMBERLAIN, LAWRENCE H.
Loyalty and Legislative Action: A Survey of Activity by the New York State Legislature, 1919–1949.
> 1st edition. Ithaca: Cornell University Press, 1951.   I 4–17
> FSL.

CHAMOUX, FRANÇOIS
The Civilization of Greece.
> Tr. W. S. Maguinness. New York: Simon and
> Schuster, 1965.   Court

CHANDLER, JULIAN ALVIN CARROLL, ed.
The South in the Building of the Nation.
> 12 v. Richmond, Va.: Southern Historical Publication Society,
> 1909–13.
> v. 1–8, 10–12   RR
> v. 9   G 5–3

CHANDLER, WALTER M.
The Trial of Jesus: From a Lawyer's Standpoint.
> 2 v. New York: Federal Book Co., 1925.   W 2–3

CHILDS, MARQUIS W.
Sweden: The Middle Way.
> New Haven: Yale University Press, 1936.   F 5–24
> marked.
> inscribed by Grover W. Ray, August 22, 1936.

CHIPMAN, NATHANIEL
Principles of Government: A Treatise on Free Institutions Including the Constitution of the United States.
> Burlington: Edward Smith, 1833.   CL B–9
> marked.

CHURCHILL, WINSTON S.
The Grand Alliance: The Second World War.
> Boston: Houghton Mifflin Co., 1950.   RR

CICERO, MARCUS TULLIUS
Brutus; On the Nature of the Gods; On Divination; On Duties.
Tr. Hubert M. Poteat. Chicago: University of Chicago
Press, 1950. F 3–17
heavily marked, personally indexed.

De Re Publica de Legibus.
Tr. Clinton Walker Keyes. Loeb Classical Library. Cambridge, Mass.:
Harvard University Press; London: William Heinemann, reprint of
1928 edition, 1948. F 3–16
heavily marked, personally indexed.

CLAIBORNE, J[OHN] F[RANCIS] H[AMTRAMCK]
*Life and Correspondence of John A. Quitman, Major-General, U.S.A.,
and Governor of the State of Mississippi.*
2 v. New York: Harper and Bros., 1860. Court

CLARK, CHARLES E.
Procedure: The Handmaid of Justice.
Eds. Charles Alan Wright and Harry M. Reasoner. St. Paul: West
Publishing Co., 1965. Court
inscribed by the editors, March 1965.

CLARK, FLOYD BARZILIA
The Constitutional Doctrines of Justice Harlan.
Baltimore: Johns Hopkins Press, 1915. B 1–32

CLARK, JOHN B[UNYAN]
Populism in Alabama.
Auburn, Ala.: Auburn Printing Co., 1927. G 7–33

another copy. G 5–32

CLARK, RAMSEY
Crime in America.
New York: Simon and Schuster, 1970. LC
inscribed by the author, n.d.

CLARK, RAMSEY and ERVIN, SAM J., JR.
Role of the Supreme Court: Policymaker or Adjudicator.
Washington, D.C.: American Enterprise Institute for Public Policy
Research, 1970. LA

CLARK, SYDNEY
All the Best in Japan, with Manila, Hong Kong and Macao.
　New York: Dodd, Mead and Co., 1960.　　I 5–41

CLARKE, JOSEPH I. C.
Robert Emmet: A Tragedy of Irish History.
　New York and London: G. P. Putnam's Sons, 1888.　　G 4–31

CLAY, HENRY
The Life and Speeches of Henry Clay.
　v. 2. New York: Greeley and McElrath, Tribune
　Office, 1843.　　G 4–25
　marked, personally indexed.

CLAYTON, JAMES E.
The Making of Justice: The Supreme Court in Action.
　1st edition. New York: E. P. Dutton and Co., 1964.　　H 3–6
　inscribed by the author, n.d.

CLEVELAND, GROVER
Letters of Grover Cleveland: 1850–1908.
　Ed. Allan Nevins. Boston and New York: Houghton Mifflin Co.,
　1933.　　G 1–6
　inscribed by John Frank, Birthday 1952.

COHEN, BENJAMIN V.
The United Nations: Constitutional Developments, Growth and Possibilities.
　Cambridge, Mass.: Harvard University Press, 1961.　　Court

COHEN, MORRIS R.
The Faith of a Liberal: Selected Essays.
　New York: Henry Holt and Co., 1946.　　I 2–24
　heavily marked, personally indexed.

Law and the Social Order: Essays in Legal Philosophy.
　1st edition. New York: Harcourt, Brace and Co., 1933.　　I 2–18

A Preface to Logic.
　New York: Henry Holt and Co., 1945.　　I 2–29
　marked.

COLLINS, CHARLES WALLACE
The Fourteenth Amendment and the States.
  Boston: Little, Brown and Co., 1912.   B 1–30

COLUMBIA BROADCASTING SYSTEM
Oyez, Oyez, Oyez: Storm Over the Supreme Court.
  CBS Reports, Part I, February 20, 1963.   W 4–34

COMINGS, L. J. NEWCOMB and ALBERS, MARTHA M.
A Brief History of Baldwin County.
  Fairhope, Ala.: Baldwin County Historical Society, 1928.   G 5–30

COMMAGER, HENRY STEELE
Freedom, Loyalty, Dissent.
  New York: Oxford University Press, 1954.   CL B 2–5

Freedom and Order.
  New York: George Braziller, 1966.   CL B–10
  heavily marked, personally indexed.

COMMAGER, HENRY STEELE, ed.
Documents of American History.
  5th edition. New York: Appleton-Century-Crofts, 1949.   CL B–15
  personally indexed.

CONFUCIUS
The Wisdom of Confucius.
  Ed. and tr. Lin Yutang. 1st Modern Library edition. New York:
  Modern Library (Random House), 1938.   F 1–27

*The Constitution of the United States of America, With the First Ten
Amendments.*
  Houston: Anson Jones Press, n.d.   I 4–32

COOKE, ALISTAIR
A Commencement Address.
  New York: Alfred A. Knopf, 1954.   I 4–34

The Corolla.
  v. 13. Buffalo: Hausauer-Jones Printing Co., 1905.   G 7–38

The Corolla.
  v. 23. Nashville: Benson Printing Co., 1916.   G 7–39

CORWIN, EDWARD S.
Court Over Constitution.
  Princeton: Princeton University Press, 1938.   B 1–33
  marked.

*Total War and the Constitution: Five Lectures Delivered on the William
W. Cook Foundation at the University of Michigan, March 1946.*
  1st edition, A Borzoi Book. New York: Alfred A.
  Knopf, 1947.   I 5–9

The Twilight of the Supreme Court.
  New Haven: Yale University Press, 1934.   Court
  marked.

COUNTRYMAN, VERN
*Un-American Activities in the State of Washington: The Work of the
Canwell Committee.*
  1st edition. Ithaca: Cornell University Press, 1951.   I 3–24
  FSL.

COY, HAROLD
The First Book of the Supreme Court.
  New York: Franklin Watts, 1958.   RR

CRAIG, ALEC
Suppressed Books: A History of the Conception of Literary Obscenity....
  Cleveland and New York: World Publishing Co., 1963   Court

CRANSTON, MAURICE
What Are Human Rights?
  New York: Basic Books, 1963.   Court
  marked.

CRITTENDEN, H[ENRY] H[USTON], comp.
The Crittenden Memoirs.
  Autograph edition, No. 7 of 100. New York: G. P. Putnam's Sons,
  1936.   G 6–15
  inscribed by the compiler, June 18, 1936.

CRONIN, A[RCHIBALD] J[OSEPH]
The Stars Look Down.
Boston: Little, Brown and Co., 1935.   I 4–19

CURRY, J[ABEZ] L[AMAR] M[ONROE]
Civil History of the Government of the Confederate States, With Some Personal Reminiscences.
Richmond, Va.: B. F. Johnson Publishing Co., 1901.   G 5–19

The Southern States of the American Union, Considered in Their Relations to the Constitution of the United States and to the Resulting Union.
Students edition. Richmond, Va.: B.F. Johnson Publishing Co., 1895.   F 5–16
marked, personally indexed.

another copy.   G 5–2

CURTI, MERLE
The Roots of American Loyalty.
New York: Columbia University Press, 1946.   I 3–8
FSL.

CURTIS, CHARLES P., JR. and GREENSLET, FERRIS
The Practical Cogitator.
3rd edition. Boston: Houghton Mifflin Co.; Cambridge, Mass.: Riverside Press, 1953.   W 4–18
inscribed by Pearl and Moose [Isenberg], n.d.

DABBS, JAMES McBRIDE
The Southern Heritage.
A Borzoi Book. New York: Alfred A. Knopf, 1959.   G 5–37
marked.

D'ARGENSON, MARQUIS [RENË LOUIS DE VOYER DE PAULMY]
Essays: Civil, Moral, Literary and Political.
1st American edition. Worcester, Mass: Thomas, Son and Thomas, 1797.   I 2–22

DAVIES, ARTHUR POWELL
The Faith of an Unrepentant Liberal.
Boston: Beacon Press, 1947.   H 3–24
inscribed by the author, January 1952.

[DAVIES, ARTHUR POWELL, *cont.*]
The Ten Commandments.
   A Signet Key Book. New York: New American Library, 1st printing,
   1956.   I 4–35

The Urge to Persecute.
   Boston: Beacon Press, 1953.   W 2–7

DAVIS, POSEY OLIVER
One Man: Edward Asbury O'Neal, III, of Alabama.
   Auburn: Alabama Polytechnic Institute, 1945.   I 5–20

DAWSON, MILES MENANDER, arranger
The Conduct of Life: The Ethics of Confucius.
   New York: Carlton House, 1915.   F 4–10

*Declaration of Independence and Constitution of the United States of
America.*
   Washington, D.C.: U.S. Government Printing
   Office, 1964.   W 2–2

DEWEY, JOHN
Logic: The Theory of Inquiry.
   New York: Henry Holt and Co., 1939.   I 5–7
   heavily marked.

*The Quest for Certainty: A Study of the Relation of Knowledge and
Action.*
   New York: Minton, Balch and Co., 1929.   I 7–8
   marked.

DICKENS, CHARLES
The Posthumous Papers of the Pickwick Club.
   v. 1 of The Works of Charles Dickens, New Century Library. London, Edinburgh, Dublin, and New York: Thomas Nelson and Sons,
   1912.   H 7–20

DICKINSON, EMILY
Poems.
   Eds. T. W. Higginson and Mabel Loomis Todd. 2nd series. Boston:
   Roberts Bros., 1892.   H 7–16

DICKMAN, WILLIAM J.
Around the Potomac.
  Alexandria, Va.: Newell-Cole Co., 1968.   I 5–45
  inscribed by the author, June 16, 1968.

DILLIARD, IRVING
One Man's Stand for Freedom: Mr. Justice Black and the Bill of Rights.
  A Borzoi Book. New York: Alfred A. Knopf, 1963.   W 3–1

DILLIARD, IRVING, ed.
Mr. Justice Brandeis, Great American.
  Saint Louis: ModernView Press, 1941.   H 3–42

DIOGENES, LAERTIUS
Lives of Eminent Philosophers.
  Tr. R. D. Hicks. 2 v., Loeb Classical Library. London: William W.
  Heinemann; New York: G. P. Putnam's Sons, 1925.   F 3–15
  marked, personally indexed.

DISALLE, MICHAEL VINCENT with BLOCHMAN, LAWRENCE G.
The Power of Life or Death.
  New York: Random House, 1965.   Court

DODD, WILLIAM E.
Statesmen of the Old South, or, From Radicalism to Conservative Revolt.
  New York: Macmillan Co., 1927.   G 2–6

DONALD, DAVID
Charles Sumner and the Coming of the Civil War.
  1st edition, A Borzoi Book. New York: Alfred A.
  Knopf, 1960.   F 5–10
  marked, personally indexed.
  inscribed by Aline and Dan Berman, February 27, 1961.

Lincoln's Herndon.
  New York: Alfred A. Knopf, 1948.   G 4–30
  inscribed by John Frank, Birthday 1952.

DONNE, JOHN and BLAKE, WILLIAM
*The Complete Poetry and Selected Prose of John Donne and the Com-
plete Poetry of William Blake.*
  Eds. John Hayward and Geoffrey Keynes. New York: Random
  House, 2nd printing, 1941.   F 8–2

DORFMAN, JOSEPH
The Economic Mind in American Civilization.
  5 v. New York: Viking Press, 1946–59.   Court

DORFMAN, JOSEPH and TUGWELL, R. G.
Early American Policy: Six Columbia Contributors.
  New York: Columbia University Press, 1960.   H 7–12

DOUGLAS, LLOYD C.
The Robe.
  New York: Grosset and Dunlap, 1942.   I 5–31

DOUGLAS, WILLIAM O.
An Almanac of Liberty.
  Garden City: Doubleday and Co., 1954.   I 1–2
  inscribed by the author, n.d.

A Living Bill of Rights.
  Garden City: Doubleday and Co., 1961.   CL B 2–4

The Right of the People.
  1st edition. Garden City: Doubleday and Co., 1958.   I 3–15
  inscribed by the author, n.d.

DOZIER, ORION T.
A Galaxy of Southern Heroes, and Other Poems.
  Birmingham: [Press of Dispatch Printing Co.], 1905.   G 6–2

Poems and Prose.
  5th edition, Memorial edition. Birmingham: [Press of Birmingham
  Publishing Co., 1927].   G 5–13

DRAPER, JOHN WILLIAM
History of the American Civil War.
  3 v. New York: Harper and Bros., 1868.   G 3–16
  marked.

History of the Conflict Between Religion and Science.
  v. 12 of International Scientific Series. New York: D. Appleton and
  Co., 1875.   F 3–20

History of the Intellectual Development of Europe.
  v. 1 of 2, revised edition. New York: Harper and Bros., 1918.   RR
  marked.

DRINAN, ROBERT F.
Religion, the Courts, and Public Policy.
  1st edition. New York: McGraw Hill Book Co., 1963.   Court

DuBOSE, JOEL CAMPBELL
Alabama History.
  Revised edition. Richmond, Va.: Johnson Publishing
  Co., 1915.   G 6–23
  marked.

DuBOSE, JOEL CAMPBELL, ed.
Notable Men of Alabama, Personal and Genealogical With Portraits.
  2 v. Atlanta: Southern Historical Association, 1904.   W 1–10

DuBOSE, JOHN WITHERSPOON
The Life and Times of William Lowndes Yancey.
  Birmingham: Roberts and Son, 1892.   G 5–4
  marked.

Du PUY, WILLIAM ATHERTON
Hawaii and Its Race Problem.
  Washington, D.C.: U.S. Government Printing
  Office, 1932.   I 4–10

DURANT, WILL
The Life of Greece.
  v. 2 of The Story of Civilization. New York: Simon and Schuster,
  1939.   F 2–13
  inscribed by Henrietta and Lister [Hill], December 8, 1952.

DURANT, WILL and ARIEL
The Lessons of History.
  New York: Simon and Schuster, 1968.   W 2–20
  heavily marked.

DWIGHT, TIMOTHY, et al., eds.
The World's Great Classics.
  11 v. New York: Colonial Press, 1899–1900.   RR

DYKEMAN, WILMA and STOKELY, JAMES
Seeds of Southern Change: The Life of Will Alexander.
  [Chicago]: University of Chicago Press, [1962].   Court

EDGERTON, HENRY W.
Freedom in the Balance: Opinions of Judge Henry W. Edgerton Relating to Civil Liberties.
  Ed. Eleanor Bontecou. 1st edition. Ithaca: Cornell University Press, 1960.   F 5–5

EDMONDS, GEORGE
Facts and Falsehoods Concerning the War on the South, 1861–1865.
  Memphis: A. R. Taylor and Co., 1904.   G 4–14

EICHLER, LILLIAN
The New Book of Etiquette.
  Revised edition. Garden City: Garden City Publishing
  Co., 1934.   I 6–22

ELIOPOULOS, NICHOLAS C.
Oneness of Politics and Religion.
  Oak Park, Ill.: privately published, 1970.   W 3–19
  inscribed by the author, n.d.

ELIOT, CHARLES W., ed.
Harvard Classics.
  50 v. (2 copies of v. 25). New York: P. F. Collier and Son, 1909–10.
  H 4–1, H 5–1

  v. 1 *The Autobiography of Benjamin Franklin; The Journal of John Woolman; Fruits of Solitude by William Penn.*
  marked, personally indexed.

  v. 2 *The Apology, Phaedo and Crito of Plato; The Golden Sayings of Epictetus; The Meditations of Marcus Aurelius.*
  marked, personally indexed.

  v. 3 *Essays, Civil and Moral, and The New Atlantis* by Francis Bacon; *Areopagitica and Tractate on Education* by John Milton; *Religio Medici* by Sir Thomas Browne.
  marked.

  v. 4 *The Complete Poems of John Milton.*

v. 5 *Essays and English Traits* by R. W. Emerson.

v. 6 *The Poems and Songs of Robert Burns.*

v. 7 *The Confessions of St. Augustine; The Imitation of Christ* by Thomas A. Kempis.

v. 8 *Nine Greek Dramas* by Aeschylus, Sophocles, Euripides and Aristophanes.
heavily marked, personally indexed.

v. 9 *Letters of Marcus Tullius Cicero With His Treatises on Friendship and Old Age; Letters of Gaius Plinius Caecilius Secundus.*
heavily marked, personally indexed.

v. 10 *An Inquiry into the Nature and Causes of the Wealth of Nations* by Adam Smith.
heavily marked, personally indexed.

v. 11 *The Origin of Species* by Charles Darwin.

v. 12 *Plutarch's Lives of Themistocles, Pericles, Aristides, Alcibiades and Coriolanus, Demosthenes and Cicero, Caesar, and Antony.*
heavily marked, personally indexed.

v. 13 *Virgil's Aeneid.*
marked, personally indexed.

v. 14 *The First Part of the Delightful History of the Most Ingenious Knight Don Quixote of the Mancha* by Miguel de Cervantes.

v. 15 *The Pilgrim's Progress* by John Bunyan; *The Lives of John Donne and George Herbert* by Izaak Walton.

v. 16 *Stories from the Thousand and One Nights (The Arabian Night's Entertainments).*

v. 17 *Folk-Lore and Fable: Aesop, Grimm, Andersen.*

v. 18 *Modern English Drama: Dryden, Sheridan, Goldsmith, Shelley, Browning, Byron.*

v. 19 *Johann Wolfgang von Goethe: Faust, Part I, Egmont, Hermann and Dorothea; Christopher Marlowe: Doctor Faustus.*

v. 20 *The Divine Comedy of Dante Alighieri: Hell, Purgatory, Paradise.*

v. 21 *I Promessi Sposi (The Betrothed)* by Alessandro Manzoni.

v. 22 *The Odyssey of Homer.*

v. 23 *Two Years Before the Mast and Twenty-Four Years After* by R. H. Dana, Jr.

v. 24 *Edmund Burke: On Taste, On the Sublime and Beautiful, Reflections on the French Revolution, A Letter to a Noble Lord.*

v. 25 *John Stuart Mill: Autobiography, Essay on Liberty; Thomas Carlyle: Characteristics, Inaugural Address, Essay on Scott.*
heavily marked, personally indexed.

v. 26 *Continental Drama: Calderon, Corneille, Racine, Molière, Lessing, Schiller.*
heavily marked, personally indexed.

v. 27 *English Essays: From Sir Philip Sidney to Macaulay.*

v. 28 *Essays: English and American.*
heavily marked.

v. 29 *The Voyage of the Beagle* by Charles Darwin.

v. 30 *Scientific Papers: Physics, Chemistry, Astronomy, Geology.*

v. 31 *The Autobiography of Benvenuto Cellini.*

v. 32 *Literary and Philosophical Essays: French, German and Italian.*
heavily marked, personally indexed.

v. 33 *Voyages and Travels: Ancient and Modern.*

v. 34 *French and English Philosophers: Descartes, Rousseau, Voltaire, Hobbes.*

v. 35 *Chronicle and Romance: Froissart, Malory, Holinshed.*

v. 36 *The Prince* by Niccolo Machiavelli; *Utopia* by Sir Thomas More; *Ninety-Five Theses: Address to the German Nobility Concerning Christian Liberty* by Martin Luther.
heavily marked.

v. 37 *English Philosophers of the Seventeenth and Eighteenth Centuries: Locke, Berkeley, Hume.*

v. 38 *Scientific Papers: Physiology, Medicine, Surgery, Geology.*

v. 39 *Prefaces and Prologues to Famous Books.*

v. 40 *English Poetry from Chaucer to Gray.*

v. 41 *English Poetry from Collins to Fitzgerald.*

v. 42 *English Poetry from Tennyson to Whitman.*

v. 43 *American Historical Documents.*
heavily marked.

v. 44 *Sacred Writings: Confucian, Hebrew, Christian (Part I).*

v. 45 *Sacred Writings: Christian (Part II), Buddhist, Hindu, Moham-medan.*

v. 46 *Elizabethan Drama: Marlowe, Shakespeare.*

v. 47 *Elizabethan Drama: Dekker, Jonson, Beaumont and Fletcher, Webster, Massinger.*

v. 48 *Blaise Pascal: Thoughts, Letters, Minor Works.*

v. 49 *Epic and Saga: Beowulf, The Song of Roland, The Destruction of Dá Derga's Hostel, The Story of the Volsungs and Niblungs.*

v. 50 *The Editor's Introduction; Reader's Guide; Index to the First Lines of Poems, Songs and Choruses, Hymns and Psalms; General Index; Chronological Index.*

ELIZABETH II
The Form and Order of the Service That Is To Be Performed and the Ceremonies That Are To Be Observed in the Coronation of Her Majesty Queen Elizabeth II in the Abbey Church of St. Peter, Westminster, on Tuesday the Second Day of June 1953.
  Cambridge: University Press, [1953].   G 6–27

ELKINS, STANLEY M.
Slavery.
  Universal Library. New York: Grosset and Dunlap, 1963.   W 1–33

EMERSON, EDWIN, JR.
A History of the Nineteenth Century Year by Year.
  3 v. New York: P. F. Collier and Son, 1900.   F 8–3
  marked, personally indexed.

EMERSON, RALPH WALDO
The Works of Ralph Waldo Emerson.
  v. 3, 4, & 5, Edition DeLuxe. New York: Lamb Publishing
  Co., n.d.   BB

EMERSON, THOMAS I. and HABER, DAVID
Political and Civil Rights in the United States: A Collection of Legal and Related Materials.
  U.S. Case Book Series. Buffalo, N.Y.: Dennis and Co., 1952.   I 4–3
  FSL.

ENCYCLOPAEDIA BRITANNICA
Book of the Year: 1968.
   Chicago: Encyclopaedia Britannica, 1968.   E

Book of the Year: 1969.
   Chicago: Encyclopaedia Britannica, 1969.   E

Encyclopaedia Britannica.
   32 v., 11th edition. New York: Encyclopaedia
   Britannica, 1910–22.   RR

Encyclopaedia Britannica.
   24 v. Chicago: Encyclopaedia Britannica, 1968.   E

World Atlas.
   Ed. Donald Hudson. Chicago, London, and Toronto: William Benton,
   1960.   W 3–1

EPICURUS
*Epicurus' Morals, Collected Partly Out of His Own Greek Text, in
Diogenes Laertius, and Partly Out of the Rhapsodies of Marcus Anton-
ius, Plutarch, Cicero, and Seneca.*
   London: printed by W. Wilson for Henry
   Herringman, 1656.   F 2–6
   marked.

ERNST, MORRIS L.
The First Freedom.
   New York: Macmillan Co., 1st printing, 1946.   I 2–16
   FSL.

ERNST, MORRIS L. and SCHWARTZ, ALAN U.
Censorship: The Search for the Obscene.
   New York: Macmillan Co., 1964.   Court

ERSKINE, THOMAS
Speeches of Lord Erskine, While at the Bar.
   Ed. James L. High. 4 v. Chicago: Callaghan and Co., 1876.   G 3–2

EURIPIDES
*Five Plays of Euripides: Alcestis, Medea, The Trojan Women, Iphigenia
in Tauris, Electra.*
   Tr. Gilbert Murray. New York: Oxford University
   Press, 1934.   F 3–21
   marked.

[EURIPIDES, *cont.*]
The Hippolytus of Euripides.
    Tr. Gilbert Murray. New York: Longman's, Green and
    Co., n.d.   F 1–24

EVERSHED, FRANCIS RAYMOND
The Practical and Academic Characteristics of English Law.
    Lawrence: University of Kansas Press, 1956.   B 1–37
    marked.

FAIRBANKS, ARTHUR
*Greek Gods and Heroes, As Represented in the Classical Collections of
the Museum: A Handbook for High School Students Prepared in Conjunction with a Committee of Teachers.*
    4th edition, revised by George H. Chase. Boston: Museum of Fine
    Arts, 1948.   F 2–12
    marked.

FAIRMAN, CHARLES
Mr. Justice Miller and the Supreme Court, 1862–1890.
    Cambridge, Mass.: Harvard University Press, 1939.   H 3–20
    marked.
    inscribed by Joseph F. Guffey, January 9, 1940.

*Famous Utopias: Being the Complete Text of Rousseau's Social Con-
tract, More's Utopia, Bacon's New Atlantis, Campanella's City of the
Sun.*
    New York: Tudor Publishing Co., [1901].   G 5–1
    marked.

FARLEY, JAMES A.
Jim Farley's Story: The Roosevelt Years.
    New York and Toronto: Whittlesey House, McGraw Hill Book Co.,
    1948.   I 2–31

FAST, HOWARD
The American.
    New York: Duell, Sloan, and Pearce, 1946.   I 4–25
    inscribed by Hamilton M. Hill, August 20, 1946.

another copy.   W 4–9
    inscribed by the author, n.d.

[FAST, HOWARD, *cont.*]
The Passion of Sacco and Vanzetti: A New England Legend.
   New York: Blue Heron Press, [1953].   I 4–27

Spartacus.
   New York: privately published, 1951.   I 5–14

FATTORUSSO, GIUSEPPE, and M. L., eds.
Wonders of Italy.
   Medici Art Series. Florence: G. Fattorusso, reprint of 11th (1952) edi-
   tion, 1953.   H 3–33

*The Federalist: A Collection of Essays by Alexander Hamilton, John
Jay, and James Madison, Interpreting the Constitution of the United
States as Agreed Upon by the Federal Convention, September 17, 1787.*
   Revised edition. New York: Willey Book Co., [1901].   W 2–19
   heavily marked.

FERNALD, JAMES CHAMPLIN
*English Synonyms and Antonyms, With Notes on the Correct Use of
Prepositions.*
   38th edition. New York and London: Funk and Wagnalls
   Co., [1937?].   W 2–12

FINDLAY, BRUCE ALLYN and ESTHER BLAIR
Your Rugged Constitution.
   Stanford: Stanford University Press, 1950.   W 1–35

FISKE, JOHN
The Critical Period of American History, 1783–1789.
   Boston and New York: Houghton Mifflin Co., 1899.   F 5–7
   marked.

FLEMING, WALTER L.
Civil War and Reconstruction in Alabama.
   New York: Columbia University Press, 1905.   Court

another copy.   G 7–19

FOLEY, JOHN P., ed.
The Jeffersonian Cyclopedia.
   New York and London: Funk and Wagnalls Co., 1900.   W 4–35

FORTAS, ABE
Concerning Dissent and Civil Disobedience: We Have an Alternative to Violence.
> A Signet Special Broadside No. 3. New York: New American Library, 1968.   CL B 2–21
> inscribed by the author, May 1968.

FOX, CHARLES JAMES
The Speeches of the Right Honourable Charles James Fox, in the House of Commons.
> Ed. J. Wright. 6 v. London: Longman, Hurst, Rees, Orme, and Brown; J. Ridgway, 1815.   G 3–1
> v. 1 & 5 marked, personally indexed,
> v. 6 marked.

FRANK, JEROME
Courts on Trial: Myth and Reality in American Justice.
> New York: Atheneum, [1949].   BB

another copy.
> Princeton: Princeton University Press, 1949.   RR

If Men Were Angels.
> New York and London: Harper and Bros., 1942.   RR
> marked.

Law and the Modern Mind.
> New York: Coward-McCann, 1949.   I 3–12
> marked, personally indexed.

Save America First.
> New York and London: Harper and Bros., 1938.   RR
> inscribed by the author, n.d.

FRANK, JOHN P.
Essays on Justice Hugo L. Black, Justice William O. Douglas, Justice Frank Murphy.
> Privately printed, 1970.   I 7–11
> inscribed by the author, February 27, 1970.

Justice Daniel Dissenting: A Biography of Peter V. Daniel, 1784–1860.
> Cambridge, Mass.: Harvard University Press, 1964.   W 2–6

Lincoln as a Lawyer.
> Urbana: University of Illinois Press, 1961.   W 3–14
> marked.

[FRANK, JOHN P., *cont.*]
  another copy.   W 2–1

Mr. Justice Black, the Man and His Opinions.
  New York: Alfred A. Knopf, 1949.   W 3–2

The Warren Court.
  New York: Macmillan Co., 1964.   W 3–18
  inscribed by the author, Fall 1964.

FRANK, JOSEPH
The Levellers: A History of the Writings of Three Seventeenth-Century
Social Democrats—John Lilburne, Richard Overton, William Walwyn.
  Cambridge, Mass.: Harvard University Press, 1955.   Court
  heavily marked, personally indexed.

FRANKFURTER, FELIX
The Commerce Clause Under Marshall, Taney and Waite.
  Chapel Hill: University of North Carolina Press, 1937.   B 1–6
  inscribed by the author, May 17, 1938.

Law and Politics: Occasional Papers of Felix Frankfurter, 1913–1938.
  Eds. Archibald MacLeish and E. F. Prichard, Jr., New York: Harcourt, Brace and Co., 1939.   H 3–22
  marked.
  inscribed by the author, October 27, 1939.

Mr. Justice Holmes and the Supreme Court.
  Cambridge, Mass.: Harvard University Press, 1938.   B 1–11
  inscribed by the author, n.d.

Proceedings of the Bar and Officers of the Supreme Court of the United
States, October 25, 1965, in Memory of Felix Frankfurter.
  Washington, D.C.: U.S. Government Printing Office, 1965.   B 1–17

FRANKLIN, BENJAMIN
The Papers of Benjamin Franklin.
  Ed. Leonard W. Labaree. v. 1 (January 6, 1706–December 31, 1734).
  New Haven: Yale University Press, 1959.   W 2–49

Works of the Late Dr. Benjamin Franklin, Consisting of His Life, Writ-
ten by Himself, Together With Essays, Humorous, Moral, and Literary,
Chiefly in the Manner of the Spectator.
  2 v. London: Longman, Hurst, Rees and Orme, 1806.
    V. 1   H 7–19
    V. 2   G 2–14

Mr. Justice Black during a light moment in his chambers at the Supreme Court

He, therefore, sent a message to him, to let him know
that he was ready to obey him as consul.

When Cinna had joyfully received his offer, naming
him proconsul, and sending him the fasces and other en-
signs of authority, he said, that grandeur did not become
his present fortune; but wearing an ordinary habit, and
still letting his hair grow as it had done, from that very
day he first went into banishment, and being now above
threescore and ten years old, he came slowly on foot, de-
signing to move people's compassion; which did not pre-
vent, however, his natural fierceness of expression from
still predominating, and his humiliation still let it appear
that he was not so much dejected as exasperated, by the
change of his condition. Having saluted Cinna and the
soldiers, he immediately prepared for action, and soon
made a considerable alteration in the posture of affairs.
He first cut off the provision ships, and plundering all the
merchants, made himself master of the supplies of corn;
then bringing his navy to the seaport towns, he took
them, and at last, becoming master of Ostia by treachery,
he pillaged that town, and slew a multitude of the inhabitants, and, blocking up the river, took from the enemy all
hopes of supply by the sea; then marched with his army
toward the city, and posted himself upon the hill called
Janiculum.

The public interest did not receive so great damage
from Octavius's unskilfulness in his management of affairs,
as from his omitting needful measures, through too strict
observance of the law. As when several advised him to
make the slaves free, he said that he would not give
slaves the privilege of the country from which he then,
in defence of the laws, was driving away Marius. When
Metellus, son to that Metellus who was general in the
war in Africa, and afterwards banished through Marius's
means, came to Rome, being thought a much better com-

Justice Black's underlining and marginal notations in Plutarch's Lives, *Vol. III*

mander than Octavius, the soldiers, deserting the consul, came to him and desired him to take the command of them and preserve the city; that they, when they had got an experienced valiant commander, should fight courageously, and come off conquerors. But when Metellus, offended at it, commanded them angrily to return to the consul, they revolted to the enemy. Metellus, too, seeing the city in a desperate condition, left it; but a company of Chaldæans, sacrificers, and interpreters of the *Augurs* Sibyl's books, persuaded Octavius that things would turn out happily, and kept him at Rome. He was, indeed, of all the Romans the most upright and just, and maintained *Octavianus* the honor of the consulate, without cringing or compli- *Rigidly adhove* ance, as strictly in accordance with ancient laws and *to ancient laws* usages, as though they had been immutable mathematical truths; and yet fell, I know not how, into some weaknesses, giving more observance to fortune-tellers and diviners, than to men skilled in civil and military affairs. He therefore, before Marius entered the city, was pulled *Marius men* down from the rostra, and murdered by those that were *murder Consul* sent before by Marius; and it is reported there was a Chaldæan writing found in his gown, when he was slain. And it seemed a thing very unaccountable, that of two famous generals, Marius should be often successful by the *Augurs* observing divinations, and Octavius ruined by the same means.

When affairs were in this posture, the senate assembled, *Senate* and sent a deputation to Cinna and Marius, desiring them *capitulates* to come into the city peaceably and spare the citizens. *to Cinna +* Cinna, as consul, received the embassy, sitting in the cu- *Marius.* rule chair, and returned a kind answer to the messengers; Marius stood by him and said nothing, but gave sufficient testimony by the gloominess of his countenance, and the sternness of his looks, that he would in a short *Marius* time fill the city with blood. As soon as the council *stern —*

the magiſtrates to call together the ſenate; and whilſt ſome ſtood round that aſſembly, inſiſting on a declaration of war againſt the Romans, others ran different ways to rouſe to arms the multitude reſiding in the country. Thus the minds, even of rational men, being hurried into imprudence by the general uproar, a decree was paſſed, that the alliance with the Samnites ſhould be renewed, and ambaſſadors ſent for that purpoſe. This haſty proceeding ſurpriſed the Samnites, who, however, inſiſted, that they ſhould not only give hoſtages, but alſo receive garriſons into their fortified places; and they, blinded by reſentment, refuſed no terms. In a little time after, on the authors of the impoſition removing to Tarentum, the whole came to light. But as they had given all power out of their own hands, nothing was left them but unavailing repentance.

XXVIII. This year proved, as it were, a new æra of liberty to the Roman commons; a ſtop being put to the practice of confining debtors. This alteration of the law was effected in conſequence of the behaviour of a uſurer, in which luſt and cruelty were equally conſpicuous. His name was Lucius Papirius. To him, one Caius Publilius having ſurrendered his perſon to be confined for a debt due by his father, his youth and beauty, which ought to have excited commiſeration, operated on the other's mind as incentives to barbarity. He firſt attempted to ſeduce the young man by impure diſcourſes; but finding that his ears were ſhocked at their infamous tendency, he then endeavoured to terrify him by threats, and reminded him frequently of his ſituation. At laſt convinced of his reſolution to act conformably to his honourable birth, rather than to his preſent condition, he ordered him to be ſtripped and ſcourged. With the marks of the rods imprinted in his fleſh, the youth ruſhed out into the

Juſtice Black's underlining and marginal notations in Livy's *The History of Rome*, Vol. II

the public ftreet, uttering loud complaints of the B O O K
depravedneſs and inhumanity of the uſurer. On   VIII.
which a vaſt number of people, moved by com-
paffion for his early age, and indignation at his Y.R.429.
barbarous treatment, reflecting at the ſame time B.C. 323.
what might be the lot of themſelves, and of their
children, flocked together into the Forum, and from
thence, in a body, to the ſenate-houſe. When the
confuls were obliged, by the ſudden tumult, to call
a meeting of the ſenate, the people, falling at the
feet of each of the ſenators, as they were going into
the ſenate-houſe, prefented to their view the back of
Caius torn with ſtripes. On that day, in conſequence
of the outrageous conduct of an individual, one of
the ſtrongeſt bonds of credit was broken; and the
confuls were commanded to propoſe to the people,
that no perſon ſhould be held in fetters or ſtocks,
except convicted of a crime, and in order to puniſh-
ment; but that, for money due, the goods of the
debtor, not his perſon, ſhould be anſwerable. Thus
the confined debtors were releaſed; and proviſion
made, for the time to come, that they ſhould not be
liable to confinement.

XXIX. In the courſe of this year, while the war
with the Samnites was ſufficient in itſelf to give
full employment to the ſenate, befides the ſudden
defection of the Lucanians, and the intrigues of the
Tarentines, by which it had been effected, they
found another ſource of uneafineſs in an union
formed by the ſtate of the Veſtinians with the Samnites. Which event, though it continued, during
the preſent year, to be the general ſubject of con-
verſation, without coming under any public diſcuf-
fion, appeared ſo important to the confuls of the
year following, Lucius Furius Camillus a ſecond Y.R.430.
time, and Decius Junius, that it was the firſt buſi- B.C. 322.
neſs which they propoſed to the confideration of the
ſtate. Notwithſtanding it had yet produced no

OVER Trading—
always brings complaint of scarcity of money. 334—340

Trade restrictions
defensible if for national defense 359-61
also to retaliate for foreign tax up our
particular goods. 361- 363-4

Sales Taxes—
are "a curse equal to the barrenness of the earth 362-363.

Politician
"Insidious & crafty animal" 365

"Capital remaining same, the demand for labor will remain the same"— this is his constant primary theme — 367

Monopolists have great influence
and abuse all who oppose their practices
and praise all who favor their ideas - 368
Do not let them suggest laws 220

Justice Black's personal indexing inside back cover of the *Harvard Classics*, Vol. 10. These notes relate to Adam Smith's *An Inquiry into the Nature and Causes of the Wealth of Nations*.

Income or Revenue goes chiefly for _rent, wages_ & profits.

Rents & wages increase with improving wealth & decline with declining wealth

Profits lowest in richest country & highest in poor & declining —

Landlords & wage earners interest identical with public — profit takers hostile to public —

Advice manufacturers & merchants must be viewed with suspicion.   pages 217–18–19–20

Natural Liberty
is subordinated to Good of all people 243

Inflation Colonial 265–6

Bankruptcy a humiliating calamity "Sound, in deed do not avoid it, as some do not avoid the gallows' 282

"The uniform, constant and uninterrupted effort of every man to better his condition, the principle from which the public and national as well as _private opulence_ is originally derived
283
289

Legal rate Interest — 298–9–94 —
3½% Govt. 4 to 4½ private persons 5% legal

Progress", "Improvement " or "Liberty" is any thing better than custom 276

"Trade is a social act." and the conduct of the trade therefore comes within the jurisdiction of society — Duty to protect from "fraud, treachery & force". 302 —
Prize fixing 303

"Men might as well be imprisoned as excluded from the means of earning their bread" 234 —

Public employment denied all but professed christians 234. note.

" do not let them abuse that precious word toleration". 234 — note

Debt to dissenters 249.

Insanity — trial of by judges & juries 274
"Justice & right" in some places means conformity to custom 276

Humboldts conditions of human development — freedom & a variety of 'situations' 279

Justice Black's personal indexing inside back cover of the *Harvard Classics*, Vol. 25. These notes relate to Mill's *Autobiography* and *Essay on Liberty*.

Centralization etc good & evil 125-6

Social motives & Social justice 149-

"men might as well be imprisoned as
excluded from the means of earning their
bread"   234

I fixed opinions "encrusting" the mind &
standing as sentinels to keep out the truth
                              244

"Teachers" and bookworms frequently study
only one side - Value of critics 248-9.

"all that makes existence valuable to any
one depends upon the enforcement of
restraints upon the actions of other people"
                              207

Men's opinions most commonly result from
their legitimate or illegitimate self interest
                              208-

Communistic opinion should be permitted
under freedom of expression 260

"among the works of man which human
life is rightly employed in perfecting and beautifying
the first in importance, surely is man himself"
                              264

Men not machines — 264
Differences in bases for trade and civil liberty regulation
                              303

Effort to emancipate slaves (1769) — 3

" Erected for their (people) use and consequently subject to their superintendence" 102.

Selfish interest inducing laws (slave-trades) 111.

" Nor is it less certain that the two races equally free cannot live in the same government" 46.

" Bonapartes dumb legislature which said nothing and did much preferable to one which talks much & does nothing" 47.

Courts Federal — 66

" Were we directed from Washington when to sow & when to reap, we should soon want bread" 66.

George Wythe 93.

" I am sensible however that the same subject may appear to different persons in very different lights. What I have urged as reasons may to sounder minds, be apparent fallacies" 162.

Lack of equipment for fight 191 – 193. 205 – 207 – 8 – 10. 214

Cincinnati order 223

Emancipation 229 —

Advice to young man 285

Preparedness 290

Agriculture — mechant marine 291

Judge Iredell died on October 2, and President Adams appointed in his place, on December 6, 1799, Alfred Moore of North Carolina. Moore was forty-four years old, had been Attorney-General of the State for five years, and was a Judge of its Supreme Court.

At its February Term in 1800, the Court decided seven cases of slight historical importance.

The last Term in which the Court sat in the city of Philadelphia was held in August, 1800, and under great difficulties; for on August 4, when the session should have begun, only Judges Paterson, Moore and Washington were present; Chief Justice Ellsworth, who had been appointed Envoy to France by President Adams, February 25, 1799, was in Europe; Judge Cushing was ill; and Judge Chase was in Maryland, engaged in electioneering for Adams in the pending Presidential campaign.[1] That the Court could no longer rely on freedom from political criticism now became manifest, when two cases were presented to it involving decisions on questions which had become political issues. In *Bas* v. *Tingy*, 4 Dallas, 37, the Court was confronted with serious questions arising out of the French spoliations on American commerce and the American retaliatory legislation of the past two years. The Federalists had insisted that a state of actual war with France existed,

Dallas, 320; that service of process should be made on the Governor and Attorney-General; that subpoenas when issued should be served sixty days before return day; and that on a failure of a State to appear, the complainant might proceed *ex parte*. Eighteen years later, in December, 1818, a bill was introduced in Congress prescribing the mode of commencing, prosecuting, and deciding controversies between two or more States; "but after debate, it was indefinitely postponed." *15th Cong., 2d Sess.*, 74, 120.

[1] Judge Chase's absence drew upon him a savage attack from the Anti-Federalist newspapers — an attack which, on the standards of today, would appear to be partially justified — for he was speaking at political gatherings in Maryland in behalf of Adams' candidacy for the Presidency. See the *Aurora*, Aug. 4, 8, 9, 11, 1800, which referred to "the Supreme Court adjourning from day to day and the business of the Nation being held up until Chase shall have disgorged himself. O Tempora, O Mores! . . . The suspension of the business of the highest Court of Judicature in the United States to allow a Chief Justice to add nine thousand

Justice Black's underlining and marginal notations in Charles Warren's *The Supreme Court in United States History*, Vol. I. (Copyright 1922, 1926, by Little, Brown and Company. Reprinted by permission of the publisher)

the culmination of a persistent search by Mr. Justice Black for a textual basis on which to predicate the maximum protection of civil liberties with a modicum of protection for interests of property. Other members of the Court have employed a double standard for interests of personality and property on philosophic grounds, but Mr. Justice Black is understandably apprehensive that such a measure of values may be fleeting over a period of time. He would therefore reject standards for which he reserves that most opprobrious epithet "natural law," [37] in favor of the compulsion of the constitutional words themselves, if in the light of language and history they can bear his reading.

Early in his justiceship he advanced the view that the "persons" protected by the due process clause of the Fourteenth Amendment are natural persons and not corporations.[38] But how were the civil liberties of natural persons to be safeguarded under the protection of "life, liberty, and property" in the due process clause unless the economic interests of such persons were to claim parallel treatment? A tentative answer seems to have been ventured in *Hague v. C.I.O.* Although the rights of assembly and freedom of speech were upheld by a majority of the Court, in a separate opinion Justices Roberts and Black united in placing the result on the "privileges and immunities of citizens of the United States" rather than the due process clause.[39] Mr. Justice Black was apparently reconciled to the conclusion that such protection under the privileges and immunities clause would be limited to citizens of the United States, excluding aliens as well as corporations; but at the same time, the clause might be interpreted to include the civil liberties enumerated in the first eight Amendments without extending the same cloak of protection to economic interests under the due process clause; that clause would presumably be left as a guarantee simply of procedural justice.

This revival of the privileges and immunities clause

Justice Black's underlining and marginal notations in Paul Freund's *The Supreme Court of the United States*. (Copyright © 1960 by Meridian Books, Inc. Reprinted by permission of the World Publishing Company)

was put to the test in reviewing the contempt convic-
tions of Harry Bridges and the *Los Angeles Times*. A
case could hardly have been more fiendishly conceived
for the purpose of testing the source of the guarantee
of freedom of speech and press, since the petitioners
were respectively an alien and a corporation. The Court
in an opinion by Mr. Justice Black found it possible
to reverse the conviction on Fourteenth Amendment
grounds; but without specifically replying to the pointed
inquiry of the dissenters who asked to be informed just
what clause of the Fourteenth Amendment was being
invoked.[40] Finally, in the *Adamson* case, the inquiry
was met by the assertion in the dissent of Mr. Justice
Black that the provisions of the first section of the
Fourteenth Amendment, taken "separately, and as a
whole," incorporate the national Bill of Rights.[41] This
position, which has not commended itself to a majority
of the Court, would achieve to the utmost the objec-
tives suggested a little earlier: a guarantee of civil
liberties to all individuals, citizens and aliens; a residue
of procedural guarantees in the vague and inclusive due
process clause; and the relegation of substantive economic interests to the discard of "natural law."

But it is one thing to slam the door of the due process clause, and another to keep it shut. Of the four
Justices who joined in the *Adamson* dissent, two—
Justices Murphy and Rutledge—were explicit in serv-
ing notice that the Bill of Rights provides content, but
only a minimum content, for the Fourteenth Amendment. Abuses may be unconstitutional though not
specifically enumerated and described. And even Justices Black and Douglas, the other two members of
the group, are not satisfied, as Professor John Frank
has acutely observed, to rest on the specific guarantees
of the first eight Amendments; for they are no less
persuaded than their brethren that, for example, criminal statutes may be unconstitutional when they are
too vague and indefinite to form a guide to conduct,

said that three artisans out of every ten had been turned adrift. Civil war seemed to be at hand; and it could not be doubted that, if once the British nation were divided against itself, France and Spain would soon take part in the quarrel.

Three courses were open to the ministers. The first was to enforce the Stamp Act by the sword. This was the course on which the King, and Grenville, whom the King hated beyond all living men, were alike bent. The natures of both were arbitrary and stubborn. They resembled each other so much that they could never be friends; but they resembled each other also so much that they saw almost all important practical questions in the same point of view. Neither of them would bear to be governed by the other; but they were perfectly agreed as to the best way of governing the people.

Another course was that which Pitt recommended. He held that the British Parliament was not constitutionally competent to pass a law for taxing the colonies. He therefore considered the Stamp Act as a nullity, as a document of no more validity than Charles's writ of shipmoney, or James's proclamation dispensing with the penal laws. This doctrine seems to us, we must own, to be altogether untenable.

Between these extreme courses lay a third way. The opinion of the most judicious and temperate statesmen of those times was that the British constitution had set no limit whatever to the legislative power of the British King, Lords, and Commons, over the whole British Empire. Parliament, they held, was legally competent to tax America, as Parliament was legally competent to commit any other act of folly or wickedness, to confiscate the property of all the merchants in Lombard Street, or to attaint any man in the kingdom of high treason, without examining witnesses against him, or hearing him in

Justice Black's underlining and marginal notations in Macaulay's *Critical and Historical Essays*, Vol. III

his own defence. The most atrocious act of confiscation or of attainder is just as valid an act as the Toleration Act or the Habeas Corpus Act. But from acts of confiscation and acts of attainder lawgivers are bound, by every obligation of morality, systematically to refrain. In the same manner ought the British legislature to refrain from taxing the American colonies. The Stamp Act was indefensible, not because it was beyond the constitutional competence of Parliament, but because it was unjust and impolitic, sterile of revenue, and fertile of discontents. These sound doctrines were adopted by Lord Rockingham and his colleagues, and were, during a long course of years, inculcated by Burke, in orations, some of which will last as long as the English language.

The winter came; the Parliament met; and the state of the colonies instantly became the subject of fierce contention. Pitt, whose health had been somewhat restored by the waters of Bath, reappeared in the House of Commons, and, with ardent and pathetic eloquence, not only condemned the Stamp Act, but applauded the resistance of Massachusetts and Virginia, and vehemently maintained, in defiance, we must say, of all reason and of all authority, that, according to the British constitution, the supreme legislative power does not include the power to tax. The language of Grenville, on the other hand, was such as Strafford might have used at the council table of Charles the First, when news came of the resistance to the liturgy at Edinburgh. The colonists were traitors; those who excused them were little better. Frigates, mortars, bayonets, sabres, were the proper remedies for such distempers.

The ministers occupied an intermediate position; they proposed to declare that the legislative authority of the British Parliament over the whole Empire was

certain tinge of democracy in the monarchies and
aristocracies of Northern Italy.

Thus liberty, partially indeed and transiently, revisited Italy ; and with liberty came commerce and
empire, science and taste, all the comforts and all the
ornaments of life. The Crusades, from which the
inhabitants of other countries gained nothing but
relics and wounds, brought to the rising common-
wealths of the Adriatic and Tyrrhene seas a large
increase of wealth, dominion, and knowledge. The
moral and the geographical position of those common-
wealths enabled them to profit alike by the barba-
rism of the West and by the civilisation of the East.
Italian ships covered every sea. Italian factories rise
on every shore. The tables of Italian money-changers
were set in every city. Manufactures flourished.
Banks were established. The operations of the com-
mercial machine were facilitated by many useful and
beautiful inventions. We doubt whether any country
of Europe, our own excepted, have at the present
time reached so high a point of wealth and civilisation
as some parts of Italy had attained four hundred
years ago. Historians rarely descend to those details
from which alone the real state of a community can
be collected. Hence posterity is too often deceived
by the vague hyperboles of poets and rhetoricians,
who mistake the splendour of a court for the happiness of a people. Fortunately, John Villani has given
us an ample and precise account of the state of
Florence in the early part of the fourteenth century.
The revenue of the Republic amounted to three hundred thousand florins ; a sum which, allowing for the
depreciation of the precious metals, was at least equi-
valent to six hundred thousand pounds sterling ; a
larger sum than England and Ireland, two centuries
ago, yielded annually to Elizabeth. The manufacture
of wool alone employed two hundred factories and

Justice Black's underlining and marginal notations in Macaulay's *Critical and
Historical Essays*, Vol. I

FRASER, ANTONIA
Mary, Queen of Scots.
New York: Dell Publishing Co., 1969.   LA

FRAZER, JAMES G.
The Golden Bough: A Study in Magic and Religion.
Abridged edition. New York: Macmillan Co., 1942.   Court

FREE SPEECH LIBRARY
Book List.
Typewritten, 1952.   I 5–1
inscribed by fifteen of Justice Black's law clerks, Fall, 1952.

FREEMAN, DOUGLAS SOUTHALL
George Washington: A Biography.
v. 1–2 of 7. New York: Charles Scribner's Sons, 1948.   I 7–1
marked, personally indexed.

FREUND, PAUL A.
The Supreme Court of the United States.
A Meridian Book. Cleveland and New York: World Publishing Co.,
1961.   W 1–43
marked, personally indexed.

FRIEDMAN, LEON, ed.
*Argument: The Oral Argument Before the Supreme Court in Brown v.
Board of Education of Topeka, 1952–55.*
New York: Chelsea House Publishers, 1969.   Court

FRIENDLY, HENRY J.
In Praise of Erie and of the New Federal Common Law.
21st Annual Benjamin N. Cardozo Lecture delivered before the Bar
Association, City of New York, January 16, 1964.   B 1–29

FROST, ROBERT
A Witness Tree.
New York: Henry Holt and Co., 1st printing, 1942.   RR
inscribed by the author, 1942.

FRYER, DOUGLAS and HENRY, EDWIN R.
An Outline of General Psychology.
  Revised edition, College Outline Series. New York: Barnes and Noble,
  1942.   G 7–23

FUNK, WILFRED and LEWIS, NORMAN
Thirty Days to a More Powerful Vocabulary.
  New York: Wilfred Funk, 1949.   W 2–16

Andrew Furuseth, 1854–1938.
  American Federation of Labor, [1938].   G 7–25

GAER, JOSEPH
The Wisdom of the Living Religions.
  Apollo edition. New York: Dodd, Mead and Co., 1956.   CL B–12
  marked.

GALLOWAY, THOMAS WALTON
The Father and His Boy: The Place of Sex in Manhood Making.
  New York: Association Press, 1922.   RR
  marked.

GARRETT, WILLIAM
Reminiscences of Public Men in Alabama for Thirty Years.
  Atlanta: Plantation Publishing Company's Press, 1872.   G 5–14

GARRISON, WILLIAM LLOYD
On Non-Resistance.
  Ed. Fanny Garrison Villard. New York: Nation Press Printing Co.,
  1924.   W 2–32

GASTON, PAUL M.
The New South Creed: A Study in Southern Mythmaking.
  New York: Alfred A. Knopf, 1970.   LA

GELBER, LIONEL
The American Anarchy: Democracy in an Era of Bigness.
  New York: Henry Schuman, 1953.   I 3–33

GELLHORN, WALTER
Security, Loyalty, and Science.
  Ithaca: Cornell University Press, 1950.   I 3–32
  FSL.

GELLHORN, WALTER, ed.
The States and Subversion.
  1st edition. Ithaca: Cornell University Press, 1952.   I 3–25
  FSL.

GEORGE, BEAUFORD JAMES, ed.
A New Look at Confessions: Escobedo, The Second Round.
  Ann Arbor, Mich.: Institute of Continuing Legal
  Education, [1967].   Court

GERRY, ELBRIDGE, JR.
The Diary of Elbridge Gerry, Jr.
  New York: Brentanos, 1927.   RR

GIBBON, EDWARD
The History of the Decline and Fall of the Roman Empire.
  Ed. H. H. Milman. 5 v., new edition. Philadelphia: Henry T. Coates
  and Co., 1845.   F 3–4
  marked, personally indexed.

another copy, v. 1   Court

GIBRAN, KAHLIL
The Prophet.
  A Borzoi Book. New York: Alfred A. Knopf, 1955.   I 5–42

GILDER, JEANNETTE L., ed.
Masterpieces of the World's Best Literature.
  v. 8 (Shelley to Zola). New York: Classic Publishing
  Co., 1910.   F 4–1

GILLETTE, WILLIAM
The Right to Vote: Politics and the Passage of the Fifteenth Amendment.
  Baltimore: Johns Hopkins Press, 1965.   LB

GOLDBERG, DOROTHY
The Creative Woman.
   Washington, D.C.: Robert B. Luce, 1963.   I 4–28
   inscribed by the author, September 21, 1963.

GOLDEN, FRANCES LEO
Laughter is Legal.
   Toronto: George J. McLeod, 1950.   w 2–18
   inscribed by Aunt George, Christmas 1950.

GOLDEN, HARRY
Carl Sandburg.
   1st edition. Cleveland and New York: World Publishing
   Co., [1961].   Court
   marked.

The Israelis: Portrait of a People.
   New York: G. P. Putnam's Sons, 1971.   LA

A Little Girl is Dead.
   Cleveland and New York: World Publishing Co., 1965.   w 1–8

Only in America.
   Cleveland: World Publishing Co., [1958].   RR
   inscribed by the author, April 28, 1959.

The Right Time: An Autobiography.
   New York: G. P. Putnam's Sons, 1969.   w 2–41

GOLDFARB, RONALD L.
The Contempt Power.
   New York and London: Columbia University Press, 1963.   Court

Ransom: A Critique of the American Bail System.
   New York: Harper and Row, 1965.   Court

GRAF, WILLIAM, comp.
Platforms of the Two Great Political Parties: 1932 to 1944.
   Washington, D.C.: U.S. Government Printing Office, 1944.   Court

GRAHAM, FRED P.
The Self-Inflicted Wound.
   New York: Macmillan Co., 1970.   LC
   marked, personally indexed.

GRANT, M[ELVILLE] R[OSYN]
True Principles of Freemasonry.
  2nd edition. Meridian, Miss.: M. R. Grant, 1916.   Court

GRAVES, JOHN TEMPLE
The Fighting South.
  New York: G. P. Putnam's Sons, 1943.   G 6–5

GRAVES, ROBERT
*I, Claudius: From the Autobiography of Tiberius Claudius, Born B.C.
10, Murdered and Deified A.D. 54.*
  New York: Harrison Smith and Robert Haas, 2nd
  printing, 1934.   F 3–7

GRAY, RANDAL LOCKHART, comp.
Wit, Wisdom and Eloquence.
  Atlanta: Harrison Co., 1930.   I 2–21

GRIGSON, GEOFFREY and GIBBS-SMITH, CHARLES HARVARD, eds.
Things. People. Ideas. Places.
  4 v. New York: Hawthorn Books, 1957.   W 4–36

GRIMAL, PIERRE
The Civilization of Rome.
  Tr. W. S. Maguinness. New York: Simon and
  Schuster, 1963.   Court

GRIMES, ALAN P.
Equality in America: Religion, Race, and the Urban Majority.
  New York: Oxford University Press, 1964.   W 2–37
  marked, personally indexed.

GRISWOLD, ERWIN N.
The Fifth Amendment.
  Cambridge, Mass.: Harvard University Press, 1955.   LA

Law and Lawyers in the United States: The Common Law Under Stress.
  Hamlyn Lectures, 16th Series. London: Stevens, 1964.   Court
  inscribed by the author, October 1964.

GROTE, GEORGE
Plato, and the Other Companions of Sokrates.
  3 v. London: John Murray, 1865.   F 2–2
  heavily marked, personally indexed.

GRUND, FRANCIS JOSEPH
Aristocracy in America.
  1st American edition. New York: Harper and Bros., 1959.   W 1–37
  heavily marked, personally indexed.
  inscribed by Edmond Cahn, n.d.

GUIZOT, FRANÇOIS PIERRE GUILLAUME
The History of Civilization in Europe.
  Tr. William Hazlitt. New York: A. L. Burt, [189–?].   F 1–18

History of England From the Earliest Times.
  Tr. M. M. Ripley. v. 5 of 5. Boston: H. A. Bolles and Co., 1876.   RR

GUNSAULUS, FRANK WAKELEY
William Ewart Gladstone.
  Chicago and Philadelphia: Monarch Book Co., 1898.   G 7–21

GWALTNEY, LESLIE LEE
The World's Greatest Decade: The Times and the Baptists.
  [Birmingham, Ala.: Baptist Book Co., 1947].   Court

HACKETT, FRANCIS
What Mein Kampf Means to America.
  New York: Reynal and Hitchcock, 1941.   I 3–26
  marked.

HALLAM, HENRY
The Constitutional History of England: From the Accession of Henry VII to the Death of George II.
  3 v., 2nd edition. London: John Murray, 1829.   D 1–2
  heavily marked.

History of Europe During the Middle Ages.
  Revised edition. World's Great Classics. New York: Colonial Press, 1899.   RR

Literature of Europe.
  3 v. London: John Murray, 1854.   D 1–3

[HALLAM, HENRY, *cont.*]
View of the State of Europe During the Middle Ages.
　3 v., 5th edition. London: John Murray, 1829. Plus 1 v. of Supple-
　mental Notes to Same, 1848.　　F 4–3
　marked, personally indexed.

HALSEY, MARGARET
The Pseudo-Ethic: A Speculation on American Politics and Morals.
　New York: Simon and Schuster, 1963.　　I 4–29

HAMILTON, EDITH
The Echo of Greece.
　1st edition. New York: W. W. Norton and Co., 1957.　　F 3–8
　marked, personally indexed.

The Greek Way.
　New York: W. W. Norton and Co., 1942.　　F 3–6
　heavily marked, personally indexed.

Mythology.
　Boston: Little, Brown and Co., reprint of 1942 edition, 1945.　　F 3–5

The Roman Way.
　1st edition. New York: W. W. Norton and Co., 1932.　　W 3–21
　marked.

HAMILTON, ELIZABETH
Memoirs of the Life of Agrippina, the Wife of Germanicus.
　2 v., 2nd edition. London: printed for John Walker
　et al, 1811.　　F 4–5
　marked, personally indexed.

HAMILTON, PETER J.
*Colonial Mobile: An Historical Study, Largely From Original
Sources . . . .*
　Boston and New York: Houghton Mifflin Co., 1897.　　G 5–8

HAMILTON, WALTON
The Politics of Industry.
　New York: Alfred A. Knopf, 1957.　　RR

HAND, LEARNED
Proceedings Commemorating Fifty Years of Federal Judicial Service by the Honorable Learned Hand.
   A special session of the United States Court of Appeals, 2nd Circuit, April 14, 1959.   B 1–28

another copy.   B 1–28

HANLEY, THOMAS O'BRIEN
Their Rights and Liberties: The Beginnings of Religious and Political Freedom in Maryland.
   Westminster, Md.: Newman Press, 1959.   I 3–6
   heavily marked, personally indexed.

HARASZTI, ZOLTÁN
John Adams and the Prophets of Progress.
   Cambridge, Mass.: Harvard University Press, 1952.   G 2–9
   heavily marked, personally indexed.

HARMAN, BOB and MONROE, KEITH
Use Your Head in Tennis.
   London: Phoenix House, 4th impression, 1959.   W 1–2
   inscribed by the author, n.d.

HARRIS, JOEL CHANDLER, ed.
Life of Henry W. Grady, Including His Writings and Speeches.
   Memorial volume compiled by Mr. Henry W. Grady's co-workers on "The Constitution." New York: Cassell Publishing Co., 1890.   F 5–14

HARRIS, ROBERT JENNINGS
The Quest for Equality: The Constitution, Congress, and the Supreme Court.
   Baton Rouge: Louisiana State University Press, 1960.   CL B 2–30
   marked.

HARRIS, SYDNEY J.
On the Contrary.
   Boston: Houghton Mifflin Co.; Cambridge, Mass.: Riverside Press, 1964.   W 1–23
   inscribed by the author, October 23, 1964.

HARRIS, WILMER C.
Public Life of Zachariah Chandler, 1851–1875.
   Lansing: Michigan Historical Commission, 1917.   I 4–12

HASKELL, H[ENRY] J[OSEPH]
This Was Cicero: Modern Politics in a Roman Toga.
   1st edition. New York: Alfred A. Knopf, 1942.   F 3–9
   heavily marked.

HAUSER, GAYELORD
Look Younger, Live Longer.
   New York: Farrar, Straus and Co., 1950.   I 5–23

HAWAII
Constitution of the State of Hawaii, Agreed Upon by the Delegates of the People of Hawaii in Convention, at Iolani Palace, . . . on July 22, 1950.
   Honolulu: Joint Legislative Interim Committee, 30th Legislature of Territory of Hawaii, July 1959.   I 3–7

HAWARDE, JOHN
Les Reportes Del Cases in Camera Stellata, 1593 to 1609.
   Ed. William Paley Baildon. London: privately printed by Spottiswoode and Co., 1894.   Court

HAYES, HELEN and FUNKE, LEWIS
A Gift of Joy.
   New York: M. Evans and Co., 1965.   I 6–17
   inscribed by Mary L. Tortorici, Christmas 1965.

HELLMAN, GEORGE S.
Benjamin N. Cardozo: American Judge.
   New York and London: Whittlesey House, McGraw Hill Book Co., 1940.   H 3–15
   marked.

HENLEY, JOHN C., JR.
This is Birmingham: The Story of the Founding and Growth of an American City.
   Copy 222 of 510. Birmingham: Southern University Press, 1960.   G 5–36

HENRY, ROBERT SELPH
The Story of the Confederacy.
  Garden City: Garden City Publishing Co., 1931.   G 5–5

HERODOTUS
The History of Herodotus of Halicarnassus.
  Tr. G. Rawlinson, revised and annotated by A. W. Lawrence. London: Nonesuch Press; New York: Random
  House, 1935.   W 1–24
  inscribed by Bennett A. Cerf, June 1938.

HERRMANN, PAUL
Conquest by Man.
  Tr. Michael Bullock. New York: Harper and Row, [1954].
  Court
  inscribed by Muriel and Powell Davies, February 27, 1955.

HERSEY, JOHN
The Wall.
  1st edition. New York: Alfred A. Knopf, 1950.   I 5–40

HEWLETT, RICHARD and DUNCAN, FRANCIS
Atomic Shield, 1947–1952.
  v. 2 of A History of the U.S. Atomic Energy Commission. University
  Park, Pa. and London: Pennsylvania State University Press, 1962.

HIBBERT, CHRISTOPHER
Charles I.
  1st edition. New York and Evanston: Harper and
  Row, 1968.   I 7–10
  marked.

HILL, BENJAMIN HARVEY, JR., and comp.
Senator Benjamin H. Hill of Georgia: His Life Speeches and Writings.
  Atlanta: H. C. Hudgins and Co., 1891.   Court
  marked.

HILL, HENRIETTA MCCORMICK
*The Family Skeleton: A History and Genalogy [sic] of the Flewellen,
Fontaine, Copeland, Treutlen, McCormick, Allan and Stuart Families.*
  Montgomery, Ala.: privately published, printed by Paragon Press,
  1958.   G 5–35

Hill, Walker H., ed.
Learning and Living: Proceedings of an Anniversary Celebration in Honor of Alexander Meiklejohn, Chicago, May 8–10, 1942.
  Chicago: privately published, 1942.   F 1–10

Hilliard, Henry W.
Speeches and Addresses.
  New York: Harper and Bros., 1855.   G 5–9

History of Freemasonry and Concordant Orders.
  Fraternity Publishing Co., n.d.   Court

Hitler, Adolf
Mein Kampf.
  Complete and unabridged, fully annotated edition. New York: Reynal and Hitchcock, 1939.   I 3–21
  heavily marked, personally indexed.

Hobbes, Thomas
Leviathan: Or the Matter, Forme and Power of a Commonwealth, Ecclesiastical and Civil.
  Ed. Michael Oakeshott. Blackwell's Political Texts. Oxford: Basil Blackwell, 1946.   F 2–16
  marked, FSL.

Hodgkins, Henry Bell
Quotes and Rhymes From Other Times.
  Pensacola, Fla.: Christ Church Parish, 1962.   I 5–44

Hoffer, Eric
The Ordeal of Change.
  New York: Harper and Row, [1963].   Court

Hofstadter, Richard
The American Political Tradition.
  New York: Vintage Books, 2nd printing, 1954.   W 1–44
  marked.

Anti-Intellectualism in American Life.
  A Borzoi Book. New York: Alfred A. Knopf, 1963.   W 4–24

HOGGART, RICHARD
The Uses of Literacy: Changing Patterns in English Mass Culture.
   Boston: Beacon Press, 1961.   W 2–27

HOLLANDER, BARNETT
The English Bar, A Priesthood: The Tribute of an American Lawyer.
   London: Bowes and Bowes, [1964].   CL B–7

HOLLOWAY, WILLIAM VERNON and SMITH, CHARLES W., JR.
Government and Politics in Alabama.
   University, Ala.: University Supply Store, 1941.   G 5–26
   marked.

HOLMES, GEORGE SANFORD
"Yes, This Is Washington!": Shrines and Sonnets of the Potomac Shore.
   Contemporary Poets of Dorrance (407). Philadelphia: Dorrance and
   Co., 1949.   I 6–35

HOLMES, OLIVER W.
*Justice Holmes to Doctor Wu: An Intimate Correspondence, 1921–
1932.*
   New York: Central Book Co., [1935].   H 3–14

HOLMES, OLIVER W. and LASKI, HAROLD J.
*Holmes–Laski Letters: The Correspondence of Mr. Justice Holmes and
Harold J. Laski, 1916–35.*
   Ed. Mark DeWolfe Howe. 2 v. New York: Atheneum, 1963.
   v. 1 marked, personally indexed.   H 7–15
   v. 2   I 5–37

HOLMES, OLIVER W. and POLLOCK, FREDERICK
*Holmes-Pollock Letters: The Correspondence of Mr. Justice Holmes
and Sir Frederick Pollock, 1874-1932.*
   Ed. Mark DeWolfe Howe. 2 v. Cambridge, Mass.: Harvard University Press, 1941.
   v. 1 heavily marked, personally indexed.   H 3–13
   v. 2 marked.   H 7–3

HOMER
The Iliad.
 Tr. Richmond Lattimore. Chicago: University of Chicago
 Press, 1962.   D 1–4

HOOD, THOMAS
Humorous Poems of Thomas Hood.
 Bound in same v. is Horace Smith and James Smith: Poetical Works.
 Ed. Epes Sargent. Boston: Phillips, Sampson and Co., 1858.   H 7–14

[HOOPER, JOHNSON JONES]
Adventures of Captain Simon Suggs, Late of the Tallapoosa Volunteers,
Together with "Taking the Census," and Other Alabama Sketches.
 Philadelphia: T. B. Peterson, 1848.   G 4–23

HOOVER, HERBERT
The Ordeal of Woodrow Wilson.
 New York: McGraw Hill Book Co., [1958].   Court

HORNE, IDA CAROLINE HARRELL
Simple Southern Songs.
 Ed. Herman Harrell Horne. privately printed, 1916.   G 5–10

HOUSER, TERZAH ADAMS
Into the Sunlight.
 New York: Henry Harrison, 1936.   G 1–11
 inscribed by the author, n.d.

HOWARD, A. E. DICK
Journeys Through Foreign Lands.
 [New York]: Record Press, [1963].   G 5–24
 inscribed by the author, August 1964.

The Road From Runnymede: Magna Carta and Constitutionalism in
America.
 Charlottesville: University Press of Virginia, 1968.   CL B–10

HOWARD, HENRY JACOB
From These Roots: The Story of North Greenville Junior College,
1892–1967.
 Tigerville, S.C.: North Greenville Junior College, 1967.   LA

HOWE, MARK DeWOLFE
Justice Oliver Wendell Holmes: The Shaping Years, 1841–1870.
  Cambridge, Mass.: Belknap Press of Harvard University
  Press, 1957.   H 3–11

HOWLETT, DUNCAN
The Fourth American Faith.
  New York, Evanston, and London: Harper and
  Row, 1964.   W 4–31
  marked.
  inscribed by the author, December 2, 1964.
No Greater Love: The James Reeb Story.
  1st edition. New York: Harper and Row, 1966.   I 2–13
  inscribed by the author, n.d.

HOYLAND, JOHN S.
They Saw Gandhi.
  1st edition. New York: Fellowship Publications, 1947.   G 1–16

HUBBARD, ELBERT, comp.
*Elbert Hubbard's Scrap Book: Containing the Inspired and Inspiring
Selections, Gathered During a Life Time of Discriminating Reading For
His Own Use.*
  New York: William H. Wise and Co., 1923.   I 6–2

HUBBARD, ELBERT, II, comp.
*The Notebook of Elbert Hubbard: Mottoes, Epigrams, Short Essays,
Passages, Orphic Sayings and Preachments.*
  New York: William H. Wise and Co., 1927.   I 6–1

HUEGLI, ALBERT G., ed.
Church and State Under God.
  St. Louis: Concordia Publishing House, 1964.   I 5–6

HUFF, MARTIN
*The Rejection of Two Carolinians: Supreme Court Nominees Parker
and Haynsworth . . . .*
  Thesis submitted in partial satisfaction of the requirements of the
  degree of M.A. in Government at the Sacramento State College. July
  13, 1970, n.p.   Court
  inscribed by the author, December 30, 1970.

HUGHES, FRANK
Prejudice and the Press: A Restatement of the Principle of Freedom of the Press With Specific Reference to the Hutchins-Luce Commission.
New York: Devin-Adair Co., 1950.   I 4–4
FSL.

HUNT, GAILLARD
John C. Calhoun.
Ed. Ellis Paxson Oberholtzer. American Crisis Biographies. Philadelphia: George W. Jacobs and Co., 1908.   G 5–22

HURST, JAMES WILLARD
The Growth of American Law: The Law Makers.
Boston: Little, Brown and Co., 1950.   G 2–1
heavily marked.

Justice Holmes on Legal History.
v. 2 of O. W. Holmes Lectures. New York: Macmillan Co., 1964.   B 1–7
heavily marked.

HUTCHESON, JOSEPH C., JR.
We March But We Remember.
Houston: Anson Jones Press, 1941.   G 4–15

HUXLEY, ALDOUS
Brave New World Revisited.
1st edition. New York: Harper and Bros., 1958.   H 1–6
marked.

INDIA, SUPREME COURT OF
Opinion of the Supreme Court of India on Special Reference No. 1 of 1964. (Reference by the President of India under Art. 143(1) of the Constitution of India Regarding the Powers and Jurisdiction of the High Court and Its Judges.)
New Delhi: Ministry of Home Affairs, Government of India, 1964.
Court
inscribed by P. B. Gajendragadkar, Chief Justice of India, n.d.

INGLIS, RUTH A.
Freedom of the Movies: A Report on Self-Regulation From the Commission on Freedom of the Press.
Chicago: University of Chicago Press, 1947.   I 3–18
FSL.

INOUYE, DANIEL K. with ELLIOTT, LAWRENCE
Journey to Washington.
   Englewood Cliffs, N.J.: Prentice Hall, [1967].   CL B 2–10
   inscribed by Daniel K. Inouye, March 4, 1968.

Isocrates.
   Tr. George Norlin. v. 1 of 3, Loeb Classical Library. London: William Heinemann; New York: G. P. Putnam's Sons, 1928.   Court

IVES, BURL
The Burl Ives Songbook.
   New York: Ballantine Books, 1953.   I 6–31

JACKSON, ROBERT HOUGHWOUT
Proceedings of the Bar and Officers of the Supreme Court of the United States, April 4, 1955, in Memory of Robert Houghwout Jackson. Washington, D.C., 1955.
   n.p.   H 3–44

JACOBS, HELEN HULL
The Young Sportsman's Guide to Tennis.
   New York and Toronto: Thomas Nelson and
   Sons, [1961].   W 1–6

JAEGER, WERNER
Paideia: The Ideals of Greek Culture.
   Tr. Gilbert Highet. 3 v. New York: Oxford University
   Press, 1945.   F 2–15
   v. 1 heavily marked, personally indexed.
   v. 2 & 3 marked, personally indexed.

JAMES, MARQUIS
Andrew Jackson: The Border Captain.
   1st edition. New York: Literary Guild, 1933.   G 4–6

Andrew Jackson: Portrait of a President.
   Indianapolis and New York: Bobbs-Merrill Co., 1937.   G 4–2
   personally indexed.

JEFFERSON, THOMAS
Democracy.
　Ed. Saul K. Padover. New York and London: Appleton-Century Co.,
　1939.　　Court
　inscribed by Felix Frankfurter, May 17, 1939.

The Life and Morals of Jesus of Nazareth.
　Cleveland and New York: World Publishing Co., 1942.　　W 4–1

*A Manual of Parliamentary Practice . . . the Whole Brought Down
to the Practice of the Present Time; To Which are Added the Rules
and Orders, Together With the Joint Rules of Both Houses of Congress . . . .*
　Philadelphia: Hogan and Thompson, 1848.　　G 2–13

*Memoir, Correspondence, and Miscellanies, From the Papers of Thomas
Jefferson.*
　Ed. Thomas Jefferson Randolph. 4 v. Charlottesville, Va.: F. Carr
　and Co., 1829.　　G 2–8
　heavily marked, personally indexed.

The Papers of Thomas Jefferson.
　Ed. Julian P. Boyd. v. 1–3. Princeton: Princeton University Press,
　1950—.　　I 7–2

JEFFERY, REGINALD W.
The History of the Thirteen Colonies of North America, 1497–1763.
　London: Methuen and Co., 1908.　　G 2–19

JENSEN, MERRILL
*The New Nation: A History of the U.S. During the Confederation,
1781–1789.*
　New York: Alfred A. Knopf, 1950.　　CL B 2–17
　heavily marked, personally indexed.

JENSEN, OLIVER ORMEROD; KERR, JOAN PATERSON;
and BELSKY, MURRAY
American Album: Rare Photos.
　[New York]: American Heritage Publishing Co., [1968].　　BB

JOHNS, WARREN L.
*Dateline Sunday, U.S.A.: The Story of Three and a Half Centuries of
Sunday-Law Battles in America.*
　Mountain View, Cal.: Pacific Press Publishing Assoc., 1967.　　Court

JOHNSON, ALLEN, ed.
Dictionary of American Biography.
  22 v. New York: Charles Scribner's Sons, 1928–44.   H 2–1
  v. 3, 4, 8, & 19 marked.
  v. 20 heavily marked.

JOHNSON, LADY BIRD
A White House Diary.
  New York, Chicago, and San Francisco: Holt, Rinehart and Winston,
  1970.   W 2–40
  inscribed by the author, Birthday 1971.

JOHNSON, ROSSITER, ed.
*Masterpieces of Eloquence: A Library of Ancient and Modern Oratory,
with Critical Studies of the World's Greatest Orators.*
  v. 1–2 & 4–10 of 10. New York: Thomas Nelson and
  Sons, 1916.   I 1–1
  v. 1 heavily marked, personally indexed.

JONES, HOWARD MUMFORD
One Great Society: Humane Learning in the U.S.
  1st edition. New York: Harcourt, Brace and Co., 1959.   I 4–24

JONES, HOWARD MUMFORD, ed.
Primer of Intellectual Freedom.
  Cambridge, Mass.: Harvard University Press, 1949.   I 3–35
  FSL.

JONES, WILLIAM CAREY
Illustrated History of the University of California.
  Revised edition. Berkeley: Students' Cooperative
  Society, 1901.   Court

JOSEPHUS, FLAVIUS
The Works of Flavius Josephus . . . .
  Tr. William Whiston. Standard edition. Philadelphia: International
  Press, n.d.   F 1–28

JOYCE, JAMES
Ulysses.
  American edition. New York: Modern Library (Random House),
  1934.   G 6–25

JUNIUS [PSEUDONYM]
Stat Nominis Umbra.
New edition. Edinburgh: printed by James Ballantyne and Co. for Vernor, Hood, and Sharpe, et al., 1807.   F 4–9
marked, personally indexed.

KALLEN, HORACE M.
The Education of Free Men: An Essay Toward a Philosophy of Education.
New York: Farrar, Straus and Co., 1949.   I 3–22
heavily marked, personally indexed.

Liberty, Laughter and Tears: Reflections on the Relations of Comedy and Tragedy to Human Freedom.
DeKalb: Northern Illinois University Press, 1968.   W 2–45
inscribed by the author, n.d.

What I Believe and Why—Maybe: Essays for the Modern World.
Ed. Alfred J. Marrow. New York: Horizon Press, [1971].   LA
inscribed by the author, n.d.

KALVEN, HARRY, JR. and ZEISEL, HANS with
CALLAHAN, THOMAS and ENNIS, PHILIP
The American Jury.
Boston and Toronto: Little, Brown and Co., 1966.   Court

KAPLAN, BENJAMIN
An Unhurried View of Copyright.
Carpentier Lecture. New York and London: Columbia University Press, 1967.   Court

KARLEN, DELMAR
Judicial Administration: The American Experience.
London: Butterworths, 1970.   Court
inscribed by the author, November 12, 1970.

KARPIN, FRED L.
The Point-Count System of Bidding in Contract Bridge.
Washington, D.C.: Council Press, 1956.   I 6–10

KAUFMAN, IRVING R.
The Message, the Medium, and the First Amendment.
The 11th James Madison Lecture, delivered March 18, 1970. New York: New York University School of Law, 1970.   Court

KENNEDY, JOHN F.
Dedication; The Gift Outright; The Inaugural Address: Washington, D.C., January the twentieth, 1961.
   No. 168 of 500. New York: printed for the friends of Holt, Rinehart and Winston, n.d.   H 7–1

Profiles in Courage.
   New York: Harper and Bros., 1956.   W 4–27
   inscribed by Simon E. Sobeloff, September 1956.

KENNEDY, JOHN F. and Others
Creative America: Collection of Photos and Short Articles.
   New York: Ridge Press, 1969.   BB

KENNEDY, JOHN P.
Memoirs of the Life of William Wirt.
   2 v., revised edition. Philadelphia: Lea and Blanchard, 1850.   G 7–30
   marked, personally indexed.

KENNEDY, JOSEPH P.
I'm For Roosevelt.
   New York: Reynal and Hitchcock, 1936.   I 2–20

KEY, V[ALDIMER] O[RLANDO], JR.
Southern Politics in State and Nation.
   A Borzoi Book. New York: Alfred A. Knopf, 1949.   I 4–2
   inscribed by Charles N. Feidelson, Christmas 1949.

KIMBROUGH, EDWARD
Night Fire.
   New York and Toronto: Rinehart and Co., 1946.   I 5–25
   inscribed by the author, August 26, 1946.

KING, MARTIN LUTHER, JR.
Stride Toward Freedom: The Montgomery Story.
   New York: Harper and Bros., 1958.   H 1–5
   inscribed by the author, n.d.

KINTNER, EARL W.
A Robinson-Patman Act Primer: A Businessman's Guide to the Law Against Price Discrimination . . . .
   New York: Macmillan Co., 1970.   Court

KIPLING, RUDYARD
Mulvaney Stories.
  Philadelphia: Henry Altemus, 1897.   G 1–13

The Recessional, The Vampire, and Other Poems.
  New York: Barse and Hopkins, n.d.   I 6–27
  inscribed by F. G. K., Christmas 1914.

KLEE, PAUL
Paintings, Drawings, and Prints by Paul Klee.
  New York: Museum of Modern Art, 1949.   I 6–14

KNOPF, ALFRED A.
Portrait of a Publisher, 1915–1965: Reminiscences and Reflections.
  2 v. New York: Typophiles, 1965.   Court

KOCH, ADRIENNE
Jefferson and Madison: The Great Collaboration.
  1st edition, A Borzoi Book. New York: Alfred A.
  Knopf, 1950.   G 2–4

KOESTLER, ARTHUR
Reflections on Hanging.
  New York: Macmillan Co., 1957.   Court

KOGAN, HERMAN
The Great EB: The Story of the Encyclopaedia Britannica.
  Chicago: University of Chicago Press, 1958.   W 1–30
  inscribed by the author, April 1958.

KOGAN, HERMAN and WENDT, LLOYD
Chicago: A Pictorial History.
  New York: E. P. Dutton and Co., 1958.   E 1–1

KOMROFF, MANUEL, ed.
The Authorized Version of the Apocrypha.
  New edition. New York: Tudor Publishing Co., reprinted from
  authorized version of 1611, 1936.   W 4–32

KONEFSKY, SAMUEL J.
John Marshall and Alexander Hamilton: Architects of the American Constitution.
New York: Macmillan Co., 1964.   CL B 2–23
heavily marked, personally indexed.
inscribed by the author, October 1964.

The Legacy of Holmes and Brandeis: A Study in the Influence of Ideas.
New York: Macmillan Co., 1st printing, 1956.   H 3–4
inscribed by the author, October 25, 1956.

KONVITZ, MILTON R.
Bill of Rights Reader: Leading Constitutional Cases.
2nd edition, revised and enlarged. Ithaca: Cornell University Press, 1960.   LC

A Century of Civil Rights, with a Study of State Law Against Discrimination by Theodore Leskes.
New York: Columbia University Press, 1961.   I 2–2

Fundamental Liberties of a Free People: Religion, Speech, Press, Assembly.
1st edition. Ithaca: Cornell University Press, 1957.   I 3–37
inscribed by the author, April 18, 1958.

another copy.   H 6–6
inscribed by the author, February 22, 1961.

KORWIN-RHODES, MARTA
The Mask of Warriors: The Siege of Warsaw, September 1939.
[New York]: Libra Publishers, [1964].   Court
inscribed by the author, July 11, 1966.

KRAFT, JAMES LEWIS
Adventure in Jade.
New York: Henry Holt and Co., 1947.   I 5–26
inscribed by the author, n.d.

KRAGEN, ADRIAN A. and McNULTY, JOHN K.
Cases and Materials on Federal Income Taxation.
American Casebook Series. St. Paul: West Publishing Co., 1970.   Court

KRISHNAMURTI, JIDDU
Authentic Notes of Discussions and Talks Given by Krishnamurti.
 Hollywood, Cal.: Star Publishing Trust, 1940.　H 7–8

The Kingdom of Happiness.
 New York: Boni and Liveright, 1927.　I 5–39

KRONENBERGER, LOUIS, ed.
An Anthology of Light Verse.
 New York: Modern Library (Random House), [1935].　RR

LaFOLLETTE, BELLE CASE and FOLA
Robert M. LaFollette.
 2 v. New York: Macmillan Co., 1953.　BB

DE LA FUYE, MAURICE and BABEAU, EMILE
The Apostle of Liberty: A Life of Lafayette.
 Tr. Edward Hyams. London: Thames and Hudson, 1956.　F 5–12
 inscribed by Asa, Jacqueline and Edgar Bates, February 27, 1966.

LAMSA, GEORGE M.
The New Testament According to Eastern Text.
 Philadelphia: A. J. Holman Co., 1940.　W 2–8
 inscribed by the author, n.d.

LARDNER, REX
The Underhanded Serve, or, How to Play Dirty Tennis.
 New York: Hawthorn Books, [1968].　W 1–7
 inscribed by Barney White, June 1969.

LASKI, HAROLD J.
The American Presidency: An Interpretation.
 1st edition. London: George Allen and Unwin, 1940.　F 1–1
 inscribed by the author, November 21, 1940.

The Danger of Being a Gentleman, and Other Essays.
 London: George Allen and Unwin, 1939.　F 1–7
 marked.
 inscribed by the author, July 1939.

Faith, Reason, and Civilization: An Essay in Historical Analysis.
 New York: Viking Press, 1944.　F 1–20
 marked, personally indexed.

[Laski, Harold J., *cont.*]
The Labour Party, the War and the Future.
    London: Labour Party, 1939.   F 1–3

Parliamentary Government in England: A Commentary.
    New York: Viking Press, 1938.   F 1–8
    heavily marked.
    inscribed by the author, n.d.

Reflections on the Revolution of our Time.
    New York: Viking Press, 1943.   F 1–6
    heavily marked.

The Strategy of Freedom: An Open Letter to American Youth.
    1st edition. New York and London: Harper and
    Bros., 1941.   F 1–2

Studies in Law and Politics.
    1st edition. London: George Allen and Unwin, 1932.   F 1–11
    marked.

Where Do We Go From Here?
    1st edition. Harmondsworth, Middlesex, and New York: Penguin
    Books (Allen Lane), 1940.   F 1–4
    marked.

Will Planning Restrict Freedom?
    Cheam, Eng.: Architectural Press, [1944].   F 1–9
    marked.
    inscribed by the author, n.d.

Lavin, John
A Halo for Gomez.
    New York: Pageant Press, 1954.   H 3–28
    marked, personally indexed.
    inscribed by Wilhelmina and Fletcher Warrey, November 30, 1955.

Law Students of the University of Virginia, Under Grant from the
Fund for the Republic, for the Committee on Civil Liberties and Civil
Rights . . . of the American Bar Association.
Municipal Actions and Civil Liberties.
    n.p., 1957.   I 4–31

Lazarsfeld, Paul F.; Berelson, Bernard; and Gaudet, Hazel
The People's Choice: How the Voter Makes Up His Mind in a Presidential Campaign.
    New York: Columbia University Press, 1948.   I 5–13
    marked, FSL.

LEE, IRVING J.
*Language Habits in Human Affairs: An Introduction to General
Semantics.*
   New York: Harper and Bros., 1941.   w 2–39

LEHMAN, IRVING
Benjamin Nathan Cardozo: A Memorial.
   Read at a meeting of the American Bar Association, July 25, 1938.
   Stamford, Conn.: printed at Overbrook Press, 1938.   H 3–17

LERNER, MAX
Actions and Passions: Notes on the Multiple Revolution of Our Time.
   New York: Simon and Schuster, 1949.   H 1–10

America as a Civilization: Life and Thought in the United States Today.
   New York: Simon and Schuster, 1st printing, 1957.   H 1–11

Ideas Are Weapons.
   New York: Viking Press, 3rd printing, 1940.   H 3–25

Ideas For the Ice Age: Studies in a Revolutionary Era.
   New York: Viking Press, 1941.   H 1–8
   marked, personally indexed.
   inscribed by the author, December 29, 1941.

The Unfinished Country: A Book of American Symbols.
   New York: Simon and Schuster, 1st printing, 1959.   H 3–27

LERNER, MAX, ed.
The Mind and Faith of Justice Holmes.
   Boston: Little, Brown and Co., 1943.   w 4–23
   marked, personally indexed.

LEVY, BERYL HAROLD
Cardozo and Frontiers of Legal Thinking, With Selected Opinions.
   New York: Oxford University Press, 1938.   H 3–18

LEVY, ISAAC D. and SMOLENS, BERNARD J., comps.
Court Is In Session.
   New York: Crown Publishers, 1950.   I 2–11

LEVY, LEONARD W.
Legacy of Suppression: Freedom of Speech and Press in Early American History.
    Cambridge, Mass.: Belknap Press of Harvard University
    Press, 1960.   CL B 1–1
    marked, personally indexed.

LEWIS, ANTHONY
Gideon's Trumpet.
    New York: Random House, 1st printing, 1964.   H 3–5
    inscribed by the author and Abe Fortas, n.d.

LEWIS, ANTHONY and the NEW YORK TIMES
Portrait of a Decade: The Second American Revolution: Civil Rights Struggle From 1954–64.
    New York: Random House, [1964].   Court
    inscribed by the author, November 9, 1964.

LIEBETRAU, PREBEN
Oriental Rugs in Colour.
    Tr. Katherine John. New York: Macmillan Co.; London: Collier-
    Macmillan, 1963.   I 6–28

The Life and History of Lewis XIV, Present King of France and Navarre.
    London: printed for John Morphew, 1709.   F 1–17

LINK, HENRY C.
The Rediscovery of Morals.
    An American Mercury Book. New York: E. P. Dutton and Co., 2nd
    printing, 1947.   I 4–23

LIPPMAN, WALTER
An Inquiry into the Principles of the Good Society.
    Boston: Little, Brown and Co., 1937.   H 5–7

LITTELL, FRANKLIN HAMLIN
From State Church to Pluralism: A Protestant Interpretation of Religion in American History.
    A Doubleday Anchor Book. New York: Doubleday and
    Co., [1962].   W 2–26

LIVY [TITUS LIVIUS]
The History of Rome.
> Tr. George Baker. 6 v., 2nd edition, corrected. London: T. Cadell and W. Davies, 1814.   F 3–3
> heavily marked, personally indexed.

LLEWELLYN, KARL N.
The Common Law Tradition: Deciding Appeals.
> Boston: Little, Brown and Co., 1960.   RR
> marked, personally indexed.
> inscribed by the author, n.d.

LOCKE, JOHN
Essay Concerning Human Understanding.
> 25th edition. London: printed for Thomas Tegg by Thomas Davison; Dublin: R. Milliken; Glasgow: Griffin and Co.; Paris: M. Baudry, 1825.   F 5–29
> marked.

Treatise of Civil Government and a Letter Concerning Toleration.
> Ed. Charles L. Sherman. Appleton-Century Philosophy Source-Books. New York: Appleton-Century-Crofts, 1937.   I 3–27
> FSL.

LOCKHART, WILLIAM B.; KAMISAR, YALE; and CHOPER, JESSE H.
Constitutional Law: Cases, Comments, Questions.
> 3rd edition, American Casebook Series. St. Paul: West Publishing Co., 1970.   Court

LODGE, HENRY CABOT
Alexander Hamilton.
> Ed. John T. Morse, Jr. Boston and New York: Houghton Mifflin Co.; Cambridge, Mass.: Riverside Press, 1898.   G 2–20

Daniel Webster.
> Ed. John T. Morse, Jr. 3rd edition, American Statesmen. Boston: Houghton Mifflin Co., 1884.   G 3–14
> marked.

LONG, HUEY PIERCE
Memorial Services Held in the House of Representatives of the United States, Together with Remarks Presented in Eulogy of Huey Pierce Long, Late a Senator from Louisiana.
> H. Doc. No. 480, 74th Cong., 2nd Sess. (1936).   G 4–13

[LONGSTREET, AUGUSTUS BALDWIN]
*Georgia Scenes, Characters, Incidents, Etc., in the First Half Century
of the Republic, by a Native Georgian.*
    2nd edition. New York: Harper and Bros., 1875.   G 6–22

LORD, JOHN
Beacon Lights of History.
    15 v. New York: James Clarke and Co., 1883–1888.   Court
    v. 1–5 marked.
    v. 2–5 personally indexed.

LOWIE, ROBERT H.
Primitive Society.
    Black and gold edition. New York: Liveright Publishing Corp.,
    1947.   F 5–4
    marked.

LUCIAN
A True History.
    Tr. not identified. London: printed for G. Hawkins, 1744.   F 3–11

LUCRETIUS
T. Lucreti Cari De Rerum Natura.
    Tr. H. A. J. Munro. 4th revised edition. London: George Bell and
    Sons, reprint of 1886 edition, 1898.   F 2–17

LYNCH, HARRIET P.
A Year Book of Southern Poets.
    New York: Dodge Publishing Co., 1909.   G 5–11

MACAULAY, THOMAS BABINGTON
Critical and Historical Essays.
    3 v., 7th edition. London: Longman, Brown, Green and Longmans,
    1852.   D 1–5
    heavily marked.

The History of England From the Accession of James II.
    v. 1 & 2 of 5, 2nd edition. London: Longman, Brown, Green and
    Longmans, 1849.   F 4–2
    marked, personally indexed.

[MACAULAY, THOMAS BABINGTON, *cont.*]
The History of England From the Accession of James II.
> v. 3 & 4 of 5. London: Longman, Brown, Green and Longmans, 1855.   F 4–4
> v. 3 marked, personally indexed.

The History of England From the Accession of James II.
> Ed. Lady Trevelyan. v. 5 of 5. London: Brown, Green and Longmans, 1861.   F 4–6

MacIver, R[OBERT] M[ORRISON]
The Ramparts We Guard.
> New York: Macmillan Co., 1952.   1 3–13
> FSL.

MacIver, R[OBERT] M[ORRISON], ed.
Great Expressions of Human Rights: A Series of Addresses and Discussions.
> Religion and Civilization Series, Institute for Religious and Social Studies. New York and London: distributed by Harper and Bros., 1950.   1 2–8
> marked, FSL.

MACKINTOSH, JAMES
Memoirs of the Life of the Right Honorable Sir James Mackintosh.
> Ed. Robert James Mackintosh. 2 v., 2nd edition. London: Edward Moxon, 1836.   H 5–6

MACLAY, WILLIAM
The Journal of William Maclay, United States Senator from Pennsylvania, 1789–1791.
> New York: Albert and Charles Boni, 1927.   1 3–30
> marked, personally indexed.

MacLEISH, ARCHIBALD
America Was Promises.
> New York: Duell, Sloan and Pearce, 1939.   1 4–37
> inscribed by the author, December 7, 1939.

MADISON, CHARLES A.
Eminent American Jews: 1776 to the Present.
> New York: Frederick Ungar Publishing Co., [1971].   LB
> inscribed by the author, April 22, 1971.

[MADISON, CHARLES A., *cont.*]
Leaders and Liberals in 20th Century America.
   New York: Frederick Ungar Publishing Co., 1961.   H 6–11
   marked.

MAHAFFY, JOHN PENTLAND
History of Greece and of the Greek People.
   Tr. and ed. M. M. Ripley. 4 v. London: K. Paul, Trench, Trübner
   and Co., 1898.   RR

MAHAFFY, JOHN PENTLAND, ed.
History of Rome and of the Roman People.
   Tr. W. J. Clarke. 8 v., International edition, copy 267 of 1000. Boston:
   Dana Estes and Co., 1883–1886.   RR

MAINE, HENRY SUMNER
Ancient Law.
   3rd American edition from 5th London edition. New York: Henry
   Holt and Co., 1883.   F 4–13
   marked.

MALONE, DUMAS
Jefferson and the Rights of Man.
   v. 2 of Jefferson and His Time, 1st edition. Boston: Little, Brown and
   Co., 1951.   G 2–2
   marked, personally indexed.

Jefferson the Virginian.
   v. 1 of Jefferson and His Time. Boston: Little, Brown and
   Co., 1948.   G 2–3
   heavily marked, personally indexed.

MANGELS, ARTHUR C. and BYERS, ALBERT F.
The Second Declaration of Independence.
   Philadelphia: Rolley and Reynolds, 1965.   W 4–28

MANN, THOMAS
This Peace: Together With the Address of November 9, 1938.
   Tr. H. T. Lowe-Porter. New York: Alfred A.
   Knopf, 1938.   I 3–1

Mannheim, Karl
Freedom, Power and Democratic Planning.
　　Eds. Hans Gerth and Ernest K. Bramstedt. London: Routledge and
　　Kegan Paul, 1951.　　I 4–16
　　FSL.

Manning, Joseph Columbus
Fadeout of Populism: Presenting, in Connection, the Political Combat
Between the Pot and the Kettle.
　　New York: T. A. Hebbons, 1928.　　G 7–37

Margolin, Robert, comp.
The Little Pun Book.
　　Mt. Vernon, N.Y.: Peter Pauper Press, 1960.　　I 5–34

Marshall, Thomas R.
Recollections of Thomas R. Marshall, Vice-President and Hoosier Phi-
losopher: A Hoosier Salad.
　　Indianapolis: Bobbs-Merrill Co., 1925.　　G 1–4

Martin, Kingsley
Harold Laski (1893–1950): A Biographical Memoir.
　　New York: Viking Press, 1953.　　F 1–5
　　marked.
　　inscribed by Henrietta and Lister [Hill], August 19, 1953.

Marx, Karl
Capital: A Critical Analysis of Capitalist Production.
　　Ed. Frederick Engles. Trs. Samuel Moore and Edward Aveling. 11th
　　edition. London: Swan Sonnenschein and Co., 1906.　　I 7–7
　　marked, personally indexed.

Mason, Alpheus Thomas
Brandeis: A Free Man's Life.
　　New York: Viking Press, 1946.　　H 3–9
　　heavily marked, personally indexed.

Brandeis and the Modern State.
　　Washington, D.C.: National Home Library
　　Foundation, 1936.　　H 3–3

[MASON, ALPHEUS THOMAS, *cont.*]
Free Government in the Making: Readings in American Political Thought.
   New York: Oxford University Press, 1949.   I 3–31

The Supreme Court: Palladium of Freedom.
   Ann Arbor: University of Michigan Press, 1962.   CL B 2–28
   marked, personally indexed.

William Howard Taft: Chief Justice.
   New York: Simon and Schuster, 1st printing, 1965.   H 3–32
   marked, personally indexed.

MASON, GENE L.
Hugo Black and the United States Senate.
   Submitted to the Department of Political Science, Graduate School,
   University of Kansas, for partial fulfillment of requirements for the
   degree of Master of Arts, May 1964. bound, typewritten.   LB

another copy.   LB

MASON, LOWELL B.
The Bull on the Bench.
   Oak Park, Ill.: Arcturus Publishing Co., 1967.   W 2–43
   inscribed by the author, March 22, 1968.

The Language of Dissent.
   1st edition. Cleveland and New York: World Publishing
   Co., 1959.   H 3–8
   inscribed by the author, May 26, 1959.

MAUROIS, ANDRÉ
Adrienne: The Life of the Marquis de LaFayette.
   Tr. Gerard Hopkins. London: Jonathan Cape, 1961.   F 5–11
   inscribed by the Bates [Col. & Mrs. E. Asa Bates], July 15, 1967.

MAWSON, CHRISTOPHER ORLANDO SYLVESTER, ed.
Roget's International Thesaurus of English Words and Phrases.
   New York: Thomas Y. Crowell Co., 1925.   W 2–5

MAYERS, LEWIS
Shall We Amend the Fifth Amendment?
   New York: Harper and Bros., 1959.   CL B 2–6

MAYHEW, JONATHAN
A Discourse Concerning Unlimited Submission and Non-Resistance to the Higher Powers, With Some Reflections on the Resistance Made to King Charles I, and on the Anniversary of His Death . . . Delivered in a Sermon Preached in the West Meeting House, in Boston, on the Lord's Day After the 30th of January, 1749–50.
    Boston: Hall and Goss, reprint, 1818.   G 3–11

MAZZUCHELLI, [SAMUEL CHARLES]
Memoirs: Historical and Edifying of a Missionary Apostolic of the Order of Saint Dominic Among Various Indian Tribes and Among the Catholics and Protestants in the United States of America.
    Chicago: W. F. Hall Printing Co., 1915.   F 5–20

McCORVEY, THOMAS CHALMERS
Alabama Historical Poems.
    Birmingham: Birmingham Publishing Co., 1927.   G 5–7
    inscribed by the author, May 12, 1919 [sic].

McCUNE, WESLEY
The Nine Young Men.
    1st edition. New York and London: Harper and
    Bros., 1947.   I 5–10

MEADE, ROBERT DOUTHAT
Judah P. Benjamin: Confederate Statesman.
    New York: Oxford University Press, 1943.   G 4–29

MEADOR, DANIEL JOHN
Preludes to Gideon.
    Charlottesville, Va.: Michie Co., 1967.   CL B 2–3
    inscribed by the author, December 5, 1967.

MEEK, ALEXANDER BEAUFORT
The Red Eagle: A Poem of the South.
    Montgomery, Ala.: Paragon Press, 1914.   I 5–36

MEIKLEJOHN, ALEXANDER
Free Speech and its Relation to Self-Government.
    New York: Harper and Bros., 1948.   I 4–21
    FSL.

MENDELSON, WALLACE
Justices Black and Frankfurter: Conflict in the Court.
   Chicago: University of Chicago Press, [1961].   w 4–16
   marked, personally indexed.

another copy.   RR

MERCK, GEORGE
Merck Manual of Diagnosis and Therapy.
   8th edition. Rahway, N.J.: Merck and Co., 1950.   H 7–23
   inscribed by the author, n.d.

another copy.   BB

another copy.
   9th edition. Rahway, N.J.: Merck and Co., 1956.   H 7–24

another copy.
   10th edition. Rahway, N.J.: Merck Sharpe and Dohme Research
   Labs., 1961.   H 7–25

*Merck Manual of Therapeutics and Materia Medica: A Source of Ready
Reference for the Physician.*
   7th edition. Rahway, N.J.: Merck and Co., 1940.   Court

MEYER, AGNES E.
Out of These Roots: The Autobiography of an American Woman.
   1st edition, An Atlantic Monthly Press Book. Boston: Little, Brown
   and Co., 1953.   G 7–15

MICHIE, ALLAN A. and RYHLICK, FRANK
Dixie Demagogues.
   New York: Vanguard Press, 1939.   G 7–20

MIDDLETON, CONYERS
The History of the Life of Marcus Tullius Cicero.
   2 v. London: printed for the author, 1741.   Court

MILL, JOHN STUART
Principles of Political Economy.
   2 v. New York: D. Appleton and Co., 1902.   F 1–12
   v. 1 heavily marked, personally indexed.
   v. 2 marked.

[MILL, JOHN STUART, *cont.*]
Three Essays: On Liberty; Representative Government; The Subjection of Women.
    World's Great Classics. London: Oxford University Press, H. Milford, [1933].   W 2–25

MILLAY, EDNA ST. VINCENT
The Harp-Weaver and Other Poems.
    New York and London: Harper and Bros., 17th printing, 1923.   G 1–14

MILLER, GEORGE MOREY, ed.
English Literature: The Victorian Period.
    New York, Chicago, and Boston: Charles Scribner's Sons, 1930.   G 1–8

MILLER, JOHN C.
Crisis in Freedom: The Alien and Sedition Acts.
    1st edition. Boston: Little, Brown and Co., 1951.   CL B 2–31
    heavily marked, personally indexed
    FSL.

another copy.   CL B 2–11

MILLER, MERLE
The Judges and the Judged.
    Garden City: Doubleday and Co., 1952.   I 2–25
    FSL.

MILMAN, HENRY HART
Life of Quintus Horatius Flaccus.
    New edition. London: John Murray, 1854.   BB

MILTON, JOHN
Areopagitica and Other Prose Works.
    London and Toronto: J. M. Dent and Sons; New York: E. P. Dutton and Co., [1927].   I 4–36

The Prose Works of John Milton, With a Life of the Author . . . .
    Ed. Charles Symmons. 7 v. London: printed by T. Bensley for J. Johnson, et al, 1806.   H 6–1
    v. 1–4 & 7 marked.

MIYAMORI, ASATARŌ, tr. and annotator
An Anthology of Japanese Poems.
   Tokyo: Maruzen Co., 1938.   G 1–2

MIZENER, ARTHUR
The Far Side of Paradise: A Biography of F. Scott Fitzgerald.
   Boston: Houghton Mifflin Co., 1951.   I 5–19

MONROE, HARRIET and ZABEL, MORTON D., eds.
A Book of Poems for Every Mood.
   Racine, Wisc.: Whitman Publishing Co., 1933.   W 2–21

DE MONTESQUIEU, BARON (CHARLES DE SECONDAT)
The Spirit of Laws, Including D'Alembert's Analysis of the Work.
   Bound in v. 2 is also Walter Bagehot: Physics and Politics, revised
   edition, 1899. Tr. Thomas Nugent. 2 v., revised edition, World's
   Great Classics. New York: Colonial Press, 1899.   F 4–6
   v. 1 marked, personally indexed.
   v. 2 marked.

MOORE, GAY MONTAGNE
Seaport in Virginia: George Washington's Alexandria.
   Richmond, Va.: Garrett and Massie, 1949.   I 3–3

MOORE, THOMAS
The Poetical Works of Thomas Moore, With Explanatory Notes, Etc.
   New York: Hurst and Co., [188?].   I 5–38

*Morals and Dogma of the Ancient and Accepted Scottish Rite of Free-
masonry.*
   Charleston, S.C.: published by the authority of the Supreme Council
   of the Thirty-Third Degree for the Southern Jurisdiction of the
   United States, 1914.   I 4–13

More Heart Throbs.
   v. 2. New York: Grosset and Dunlap, 1911.   I 5–30

MORGAN, DONALD G.
Congress and the Constitution: A Study of Responsibility.
   Cambridge, Mass.: Belknap Press of Harvard University
   Press, 1966.   Court

MORGAN, EDMUND S.
The Birth of the Republic.
  Chicago: University of Chicago Press; Toronto: University of Toronto Press, 11th impression, 1964.   W 2-17
  heavily marked.

MORGAN, JOHN TYLER and PETTUS, EDMUND WINSTON
*Memorial Addresses in the Senate of the United States, April 18, 1908
and in the House of Representatives, April 25, 1908.*
  Washington, D.C.: U.S. Government Printing Office, 1909.   Court

MORGAN, JOY ELMER, ed.
The American Citizens Handbook.
  6th revised edition. Washington, D.C.: National Council for the Social
  Studies, [1968].   CL B 2-19

MORRIS, RICHARD B., ed.
Four Hundred Notable Americans.
  Chief consulting ed. Henry Steele Commager. Perennial Library.
  New York and Evanston: Harper and Row, [1965].   I 4-38

MOTT, RODNEY L.
Due Process of Law.
  Indianapolis: Bobbs-Merrill Co., 1926.   W 4-15
  marked, personally indexed.

MULLER, HERBERT JOSEPH
The Uses of the Past: Profiles of Former Societies.
  A Mentor Book. New York: Oxford University
  Press, [1957].   F 5-18

MULLER, LEON ARNOLD
Spirit of Youth: Universal Secular Art.
  New York: Exposition Press, [1965].   LB
  inscribed by the author, September 17, 1971.

MUNRO, WILLIAM BENNETT
The Governments of Europe.
  New and revised edition. New York: Macmillan Co., 1931.   H 6-4
  marked, personally indexed.

NASH, OGDEN
Versus.
  Boston: Little, Brown and Co., 1950.   I 2–6

NATIONAL GEOGRAPHIC MAGAZINE
Everyday Life in Ancient Times: Highlights of the Beginnings of West-
ern Civilization in Mesopotamia, Egypt, Greece, and Rome.
  Washington, D.C.: National Geographic Society, 1951.   F I–23
  inscribed by Tom Corcoran, August 20, 1951.

NATIONAL LEAGUE OF AMERICAN PEN WOMEN,
ALABAMA MEMBERS
Historic Homes of Alabama and Their Traditions.
  Birmingham: Birmingham Publishing Co., 1935.   G 6–4

NEHRU, B[RAJ] K[UMAR]
Speaking of India.
  Washington, D.C.: Information Service of India, [1963?].   G 7–22

NEUBERGER, RICHARD L. and KAHN, STEPHEN B.
Integrity: The Life of George W. Norris.
  New York: Vanguard Press, 1937.   H I–7

NEVINS, ALLAN
Grover Cleveland: A Study in Courage.
  New York: Dodd, Mead and Co., 1932.   G 4–4
  marked, personally indexed.

NEW YORK CITY ASSOCIATION OF THE BAR, SPECIAL COMMITTEE
ON THE STUDY OF COMMITMENT PROCEDURES AND THE LAW
RELATING TO INCOMPETENTS
Mental Illness, Due Process, and the Criminal Defendant: A Second Re-
port and Additional Recommendations . . . .
  New York: Fordham University Press, 1968.   Court

NEW YORK, SUPREME COURT OF THE STATE OF
Exercises on the Occasion of the 250th Anniversary of its Founding:
Albany, New York, May 28, 1941.
  Stamford, Conn.: Overbrook Press, 1941.   W 3–13

NEWMAN, JAMES R.
The Rule of Folly.
    New York: Simon and Schuster, 1962.   W 4–20
    inscribed by the author, January 15, 1962.

NIXON, HERMAN CLARENCE
Forty Acres and Steel Mules.
    Chapel Hill: University of North Carolina Press, 1938.   H 1–3
    inscribed by the author, n.d.

NOONAN, JOHN T., ed.
The Morality of Abortion: Legal and Historical Perspectives.
    Cambridge, Mass.: Harvard University Press, 1970.   Court

NORRIS, GEORGE W.
Peace Without Hate: A Lecture Delivered at the University of Ne-
braska.
    Lincoln: University of Nebraska Press, 1943.   Court
    inscribed by John Carson, October 14, 1949.

NORRIS, HAROLD
Mr. Justice Murphy and the Bill of Rights.
    Dobbs Ferry, N.Y.: Oceana Publications, 1965.   B 1–5
    inscribed by the author, March 1966.

NORTHROP, F[ILMER] S[TUART] C[UCKOW]
The Complexity of Legal and Ethical Experience: Studies in the Method
of Normative Subjects.
    1st edition. Boston and Toronto: Little, Brown and
    Co., 1959.   F 5–3

NORTON, CHARLES LEDYARD
Political Americanisms.
    New York and London: Longman's, Green and Co., 1890.   W 2–9

NORTON, THOMAS JAMES
The Constitution of the United States: Its Sources and Its Application.
    Special edition. Cleveland and New York: World Publishing Co.,
    [1940].   W 2–15

[Norton, Thomas James, *cont.*]
another copy.
  New York: Nesterman Publishing Co., 10th
  printing, 1945.   w 2–29
  marked, personally indexed.

Nowell-Smith, Patrick Horace
Ethics.
  A Pelican Book. Melbourne, London, and Baltimore: Penguin Books,
  [1961].   w 1–42

Oates, James F., Jr.
Business and Social Change: Life Insurance Looks to the Future.
  New York: McGraw Hill, [1968].   Court

O'Connor, Basil
Man's Responsibility in the Fight Against Disease.
  Address . . . delivered at the Second International Poliomyelitis Conference, Copenhagen, Denmark, September 1951.   I 5–8
  inscribed by the author, n.d.

Ogden, August Raymond
*The Dies Committee: A Study of the Special House Committee for the
Investigation of Un-American Activities, 1938–1944.*
  2nd revised edition. Washington, D.C.: Catholic University Press,
  1945.   I 3–14
  FSL.

Ogg, Frederic Austin
English Government and Politics.
  New York: Macmillan Co., 1929.   w 1–22

Orations of British Orators.
  2 v., revised edition, World's Great Classics. New York: Colonial
  Press, 1900.   I 1–3
  v. 2 marked.

Oriental Treasures: Wisdom From the Great Inspirational Books of Asia.
  Kansas City, Missouri: Hallmark Cards, 1967.   w 2–48

OSTERWEIS, ROLLIN G.
Romanticism and Nationalism in the Old South.
Yale Historical Publications, Miscellany, 49. New Haven: Yale University Press, 1949. 1 4–5

OWEN, MARIE BANKHEAD, comp.
Our State: Alabama.
Alabama State Department of Archives and History, Historical and Patriotic Series, No. 7. Birmingham: Birmingham Printing Co., 1927. G 5–34
inscribed by the compiler, September 1, 1927.

OWEN, THOMAS McADORY
History of Alabama and Dictionary of Alabama Biography.
4 v. Chicago: S. J. Clarke Publishing Co., 1921. G 6–1

PADOVER, SAUL K., ed.
Thomas Jefferson and the National Capital, 1783–1818.
Washington, D.C.: U.S. Government Printing Office, 1946. Court

To Secure These Blessings: The Great Debates of the Constitutional Convention of 1787.
A Ridge Press Book. New York: Washington Square Press, 1970. LA
inscribed by the author, June 21, 1971.

PAINE, THOMAS
The Writings of Thomas Paine.
Ed. Carl Van Doren. New York: Boni and Liveright, 1922. BB
FSL.

PARES, BERNARD
Russia: Its Past and Present.
A Mentor Book. [New York]: New American Library, [1962]. W 1–39

PARRINGTON, VERNON LOUIS
The Beginnings of Critical Realism in America, 1860–1920.
v. 3 of Main Currents in American Thought, 1st edition. New York: Harcourt, Brace and Co., 1930. G 3–9
marked.

[PARRINGTON, VERNON LOUIS, *cont.*]
Main Currents in American Thought.
New York: Harcourt, Brace and Co., 1943.   G 7–29
heavily marked, personally indexed.

PARSONS, EDWARD ALEXANDER
The Alexandrian Library: Glory of the Hellenic World.
Amsterdam and New York: Elsevier Press, 1952.   RR
marked, personally indexed.

PARTON, JAMES
Life of Andrew Jackson.
3 v. Boston and New York: Houghton Mifflin Co., 1887–88.   G 4–5

PASCHAL, JOEL FRANCIS
Mr. Justice Sutherland.
Princeton: Princeton University Press, 1951.   B 1–13

PATER, ALAN F. and LANDAU, MILTON, comps. and arrangers
What They Said in 1937: The Yearbook of Oral Opinion.
New York: Paebar Co., 1937.   I 5–29

PEARE, CATHERINE OWENS
The Louis D. Brandeis Story.
New York: Thomas Y. Crowell Co., 1970.   I 3–2

PEARSON, DREW and ANDERSON, JACK
The Case Against Congress: A Compelling Indictment of Corruption on Capitol Hill.
New York: Simon and Schuster, 1st printing, 1968.   H 7–9

PERRY, RALPH BARTON
The Thought and Character of William James.
Briefer version. New York: George Braziller, 1954.   G 4–1
marked.

PETERSEN, SVEND, comp.
Mark Twain and the Government.
Caldwell, Idaho: Caxton Printers, 1960.   RR

PETERSON, HOUSTON, ed.
A Treasury of the World's Great Speeches.
  New York: Simon and Schuster, 1st printing, 1954.   I 2–10

PFEFFER, LEO
Church, State, and Freedom.
  Boston: Beacon Press, 1953.   I 4–7

The Liberties of an American: The Supreme Court Speaks.
  Boston: Beacon Press, 1956.   I 5–27

Physicians' Desk Reference to Pharmaceutical Specialties and Biologicals.
  17th edition. Oradell, N.J.: Medical Economics, 1962.   H 7–22

PICKETT, ALBERT JAMES
History of Alabama, and Incidentally of Georgia and Mississippi, From the Earliest Period.
  Birmingham: Webb Book Co., 1900.   G 4–22

PIKE, ALBERT
Hymns to the Gods and Other Poems.
  Ed. Lilian Pike Roome. Little Rock: Fred W.
  Allsopp, 1916.   G 5–12

[PINKERTON, JOHN]
The Treasury of Wit.
  Tr. H. Bennet [pseudonym]. 2 v. London: printed for C. Dilly in Poultry and Thomas Evans in Paternoster Row, 1786.   W 2–31

PIONEERS CLUB
Early Days in Birmingham: A Printing of the Original Papers of the Pioneers Club Whose Members Were Eye-Witnesses to the Events of the Founding of the City.
  Copy 218 of 500. Birmingham: Southern University
  Press, 1968.   G 5–20

PLATO
Apology, Crito, Republic I–II.
  Chicago: Great Books Foundation, n.d.   F 1–25

[PLATO, *cont.*]
Dialogues of Plato.
   Tr. Benjamin Jowett. revised edition. New York: Colonial
   Press, 1899.   F 2–4

The Dialogues of Plato.
   Tr. Benjamin Jowett. 2 v. New York: Random
   House, 1937.   F 2–1
   marked, personally indexed.

Plato's The Republic.
   Tr. Benjamin Jowett. New York: Modern Library (Random House),
   [1941].   I 3–11
   FSL.

PLUTARCH
Plutarch's Lives: The Lives of the Noble Grecians and Romans.
   Tr. John Dryden, revisor Arthur Hugh Clough. New York: Modern
   Library (Random House), [1932].   Court

Plutarch's Lives: The Translation Called Dryden's.
   Revisor Arthur Hugh Clough. 5 v. London: Sampson Low, Marston,
   Low, and Searle, 1874.   F 4–4
   v. 1, 3, 4, & 5 marked.
   v. 1, 3, & 5 personally indexed.

Plutarch's Writings: Essays and Miscellaneous.
   Eds. Arthur Hugh Clough and William W. Goodwin. 5 v. New York
   and Pittsburgh: Colonial Co., 1905.   W 3–10
   v. 2 & 5 marked.

POLWHELE, RICHARD, tr.
The Idyllia, Epigrams, and Fragments of Theocritus, Bion, and Moschus,
With the Elegies of Tyrtaeus.
   New edition, corrected. Bath: printed by R.
   Cruttwell, 1791.   F 1–16

POPE JOHN XXIII
Mater et Magistra: An Encyclical Letter of His Holiness.
   Chicago: Discoverer Press, [1962].   CL B–8
   marked.

POTTER, JOHN
Archaeologica Graeca, or, the Antiquities of Greece.
   2 v. Edinburgh: printed for Mundell, Doig, and Stevenson, and Others, 1808.   F 2–3

POUND, ROSCOE
The Task of Law.
  Lancaster, Pa.: Franklin and Marshall College, 1944.   W 2–35
  marked, personally indexed.

POWELL, MARY G.
The History of Old Alexandria, Virginia, From July 13, 1749 to May 24, 1861.
  Richmond, Va.: William Byrd Press, 1928.   I 6–11
  inscribed by the author, October 18, 1928.

PRESCOTT, WILLIAM H.
History of the Reign of Ferdinand and Isabella, the Catholic.
  v. 1 of 2, 3rd edition. New York: A. L. Burt Co., n.d.   I 7–3
  heavily marked.

PRINGLE, HENRY F.
The Life and Times of William Howard Taft.
  2 v. New York: J. J. Little and Ives Co., 1939.   B 1–2
  heavily marked, personally indexed.

PROCOPIUS
Secret History of Procopius.
  Tr. Richard Atwater. New York: Covici Friede, 1934.   F 2–20
  marked, personally indexed.

PROXMIRE, ELLEN
One Foot in Washington: The Perilous Life of a Senator's Wife.
  Washington, D.C.: Robert B. Luce, 1963.   I 6–41

PUTNAM, CARLETON
High Journey: A Decade in the Pilgrimage of an Air Line Pioneer.
  New York: Charles Scribner's Sons, 1945.   I 5–21
  inscribed by the author, n.d.

QUIGLEY, CARROLL
The Evolution of Civilizations.
  New York: Macmillan Co., 1961.   Court
  inscribed by the author, n.d.

Tragedy and Hope: A History of the World in Our Time.
  New York: Macmillan Co., 1966.   W 1–21

RADIN, MAX
The Day of Reckoning.
    New York: Alfred A. Knopf, 1943.   BB

RAMASWAMY, M.
Some Suggestions for the Modification of the Draft Constitution of India.
    Basavangudi, Bangalore: Gokhale Institute of Public
    Affairs, 1948.   G 7–5

RAMO, SIMON
Extraordinary Tennis for the Ordinary Player: Winning Strategy for the Tennis Enthusiast Who Plays for Fun.
    New York: Crown Publishers, 1970.   I 5–12
    inscribed by Martha and Johnny, n.d.

RAND MCNALLY
Ideal Atlas of the World.
    Chicago and New York: Rand McNally, 1921.   W 3–32

Road Atlas: U.S., Canada, Mexico.
    Rand McNally, 1960.   W 3–34

another copy.   W 3–35

REED, ALBERT GRANBERRY, ed.
English Literature: The Romantic Period.
    New York, Chicago, and Boston: Charles Scribner's
    Sons, 1929.   G 1–9

REEL, A. FRANK
The Case of General Yamashita.
    Chicago: University of Chicago Press, 1949.   I 6–43

REICH, CHARLES A.
The Greening of America.
    New York: Random House, 1970.   LB
    heavily marked.
    inscribed by the author, October 24, 1970.

REMBAR, CHARLES
The End of Obscenity: The Trials of Lady Chatterley, Tropic of Cancer and Fanny Hill.
New York: Random House, 1968.   RR

RESTON, JAMES
Sketches in the Sand.
New York: Alfred A. Knopf, 1967.   BB

RICHARDSON, JAMES D., comp.
A Compilation of the Messages and Papers of the Confederacy.
2 v. Nashville: U.S. Publishing Co., 1906.   H 1–2

A Compilation of the Messages and Papers of the Presidents, 1789–1897.
10 v. Washington, D.C.: U.S. Government Printing Office, 1896–99.
H 1–1
v. 1, 2, 6, & 9 marked, personally indexed.

RILEY, BENJAMIN FRANKLIN
History of the Baptists of Alabama: From the Time of Their First Occupation of Alabama in 1808 Until 1894 . . . .
Birmingham: Roberts and Son, 1895.   G 5–15

A Memorial History of the Baptists of Alabama . . . .
Philadelphia: printed for Alabama Baptist State Convention by Judson Press, 1923.   G 5–23

ROBERTSON, J[OHN] M[ACKINNON]
The Evolution of States: An Introduction to English Politics.
New York and London: G. P. Putnam's Sons, 1913.   F 1–19
heavily marked, personally indexed.

ROBINSON, CHARLES A., JR., ed.
An Anthology of Greek Drama.
New York and Toronto: Rinehart and Co., 1953.   F 5–13
marked.

ROBINSON, VICTOR
The New People's Physician: The Concise Encyclopedia of Health.
　8 v. New York: William H. Wise and Co., 1941.　　H 7–21
　v. 1 & 2 marked.

RODELL, FRED
Fifty-Five Men: The Story of the American Constitution.
　1st edition. New York and Harrisburg, Pa.: Telegraph
　Press, 1936.　　W 4–14

Her Infinite Variety: Portraits of Thirty-Six Women Around the World.
　Garden City: Doubleday and Co., [1966].　　BB
　inscribed by the author, February 1967.

Nine Men: A Political History of the Supreme Court of the U.S. from 1790–1955.
　New York: Random House, 1955.　　B 1–9
　inscribed by the author, August 1955.

Woe Unto You, Lawyers!
　New York: Reynal and Hitchcock, 1939.　　F 5–1
　inscribed by the author, n.d.

ROGGE, O. JOHN
The First and the Fifth, With Some Excursions Into Others.
　New York and Toronto: Thomas Nelson and Sons, 1960.　　I 4–11

ROLLIN, CHARLES
The Ancient History of the Egyptians, Carthaginians, Assyrians, Babylonians, Medes and Persians, Macedonians and Grecians.
　2 v. Philadelphia: E. Claxton and Co., 1882.　　F 1–29

ROMM, ALEXANDER
Matisse: A Social Critique.
　Tr. Jack Chen. New York: Lear, 1947.　　I 5–11

ROOSEVELT, ELLIOTT
As He Saw It.
　New York: Duell, Sloan, and Pearce, [1946].　　I 5–43

Roosevelt, Franklin Delano
Development of United States Foreign Policy: Addresses and Messages of Franklin D. Roosevelt . . . .
   S. Doc. No. 188, 77th Cong., 2nd Sess. (1942).   I 7–4

Roosevelt, Franklin Delano and Pius XII
Wartime Correspondence Between President Roosevelt and Pope Pius XII.
   New York: Macmillan Co., 1947.   I 2–30

Rosenkranz, Joseph Aaron
Sixty Stray Thoughts Jotted Down Along the Avenue of Life.
   Los Angeles: employees of National Schools, 1943.   W 1–36

Ross, Malcolm
All Manner of Men: The Racial Crisis in American Life.
   New York: Reynal and Hitchcock, 1948.   H 1–4
   inscribed by the author, June 11, 1948.

Death of a Yale Man.
   New York and Toronto: Farrar and Rinehart, 1939.   F 1–22
   marked, personally indexed.

Rossiter, Clinton
The Supreme Court and the Commander-in-Chief.
   Ithaca: Cornell University Press, 1951.   B 1–31

Rostow, Eugene V.
The Sovereign Prerogative: The Supreme Court and the Quest for Law.
   New Haven and London: Yale University Press, 1962.   W 4–30
   inscribed by the author, October 1962.

Rothfels, Hans
The German Opposition to Hitler.
   The Humanist Library. Hinsdale, Ill.: Henry Regnery Co., 1948.
   Court

Runes, Dagobert D.
The Disinherited and the Law.
   New York: Philosophical Library, 1964.   CL B 2–27

Runes, Dagobert D., ed.
Dictionary of Philosophy: Ancient, Medieval, Modern.
   Ames, Iowa: Littlefield, Adams and Co., 1955.   F 5–19

Russell, Bertrand
Education and the Good Life.
   New York: Boni and Liveright, 1926.   BB

Political Ideals.
   New York: Century Co., 1917.   I 7–5
   marked.

Rutledge, Wiley [Blount]
A Declaration of Legal Faith.
   Lawrence: University of Kansas Press, 1947.   B 1–36

*Proceedings in the U.S. Supreme Court in Memory of Wiley Blount
Rutledge, April 10, 1951.*
   Washington, D.C.: U.S. Government
   Printing Office, 1951.   H 3–34

Ryan, Abram J.
Father Ryan's Poems.
   Mobile, Ala.: J. L. Rapier and Co., 1879.   G 6–12

Ryan, John A.
Questions of the Day.
   Boston: Stratford Co., 1931.   H 1–9
   inscribed by the author, March 24, 1942.

Sacco, Nicola and Vanzetti, Bartolomeo
The Letters of Sacco and Vanzetti.
   Eds. Marion Denman Frankfurter and Gardner Jackson. New York:
   Viking Press, 2nd printing, 1928.   I 5–22

Salinger, Pierre and Vanocur, Sander, eds.
A Tribute to John F. Kennedy.
   Chicago: Encyclopaedia Britannica, 1964.   H 6–7

SAMPLE, ROBERT FLEMING
Beacon-Lights of the Reformation, or, Romanism and the Reformers.
Philadelphia: Presbyterian Board of Publication and Sabbath-School
Work, [1889]. Court

SANDBURG, CARL
An Address Before a Joint Session of Congress, February 12, 1959.
New York: Harcourt, Brace and Co., [1959]. Court
inscribed by the author, n.d.

Remembrance Rock.
1st regular edition. New York: Harcourt, Brace and
Co., 1948. I 7–6
marked.
inscribed by the author, n.d.

SANDERSON, EDGAR; LAMBERTON, JOHN PORTER;
MORRIS, CHARLES; and Others
Literature of the 19th Century.
v. 9 of The History and Progress of the World. Philadelphia: Thomas
Noland, 1913. RR

Sandlapper 1968: The Magazine of South Carolina.
Ed. Robert Pierce Wilkins, 1968. Court
inscribed by Broadus R., Sr., Evelyn H.,
Ricky, Anne, Margaret and Dick Littlejohn, n.d.

DE SANTILLANA, GIORGIO
The Crime of Galileo.
Chicago: University of Chicago Press, 1955. G 7–17
heavily marked, personally indexed.

SCHLESINGER, ARTHUR M.
Paths to the Present.
Boston: Houghton Mifflin Co.; Cambridge, Mass.: Riverside Press,
1964. CL B–6
personally indexed.

SCHLESINGER, ARTHUR M., JR.
The Age of Jackson.
Boston: Little, Brown and Co., 1945. G 4–8
heavily marked, personally indexed.
inscribed by Sidney Davis, December 25, 1945.

[SCHLESINGER, ARTHUR M., JR., *cont.*]
The Politics of Hope.
  Boston: Houghton Mifflin Co.; Cambridge, Mass.: Riverside Press, 1963.   W 1–12

The Vital Center.
  Sentry edition. Boston: Houghton Mifflin Co.; Cambridge, Mass.: Riverside Press, 1962.   CL B 2–24

SCHMULOWITZ, NAT
The Laws of the Town of San Francisco, 1847.
  San Francisco: privately printed, 1949.   1 5–3

SCHROEDER, THEODORE
A Challenge to Sex Censors.
  New York: privately printed, 1938.   W 1–28

SCHUBERT, GLENDON A.
Constitutional Politics: The Political Behavior of Supreme Court Justices and the Constitutional Politics That They Make.
  New York: Holt, Rinehart, and Winston, 1960.   F 5–27

SCHUCKERS, J[ACOB] W.
The Life and Public Services of Salmon Portland Chase.
  New York: D. Appleton and Co., 1874.   H 1–12

SCHWARTZ, BERNARD
A Commentary on the Constitution of the United States.
  2 v. of 5. New York: Macmillan Co., [1963–68].   CL B 2–9
  inscribed by the author, n.d.

SCOTT, WINIFRED
Is Your Death Inevitable?
  New York: Pageant Press, n.d.   Court
  inscribed by the author, n.d.

SEAGLE, WILLIAM
The Quest for Law.
  A Borzoi Book. New York: Alfred A. Knopf, 1941.   W 3–9
  heavily marked.

SEAY, B[URWELL] W[ARREN], IV
Descendants of Abraham Seay and Seay Miscellany.
  v. 2. Burwell Warren Seay, IV, 1971.   W 1–14

The Secret of the Golden Flower: A Chinese Book of Life.
  Tr. Cary F. Baynes. New York: Harcourt, Brace and Co., 3rd impression, 1935.   I 6–3

SELDES, GEORGE
The Facts Are: A Guide to Falsehood and Propaganda in the Press and Radio.
  New York: In Fact, 2nd printing, 1942.   I 6–4
  marked, personally indexed.
  inscribed by the author, n.d.

Freedom of the Press.
  Garden City: Garden City Publishing Co., 1937.   I 3–17

SELDES, GILBERT
The Great Audience.
  New York: Viking Press, 1951.   I 3–29
  FSL.

DE SÉLINCOURT, AUBREY
The World of Herodotus.
  1st American edition. Boston and Toronto: Little, Brown and Co., 1962.   F 1–21
  heavily marked, personally indexed.

SELSAM, HOWARD
What is Philosophy? A Marxist Introduction.
  2nd revised edition. New York: International Publishers, 1939.   I 5–17

SENECA, [LUCIUS ANNAEUS]
The Morals of Seneca: A Selection of His Prose.
  Ed. Walter Clode. London: Walter Scott, 1888.   F 2–9
  marked.

Seneca's Morals: By Way of Abstract, to Which is Added a Discourse Under the Title of an After-Thought.
  Ed. Roger L'Estrange, new edition. London: printed for S. Crowder, etc., 1793.   F 2–8
  marked.

SEYMOUR, WHITNEY NORTH
The Obligations of the Lawyer to His Profession.
   25th Annual Benjamin Cardozo Lecture delivered before the Asso-
   ciation of the Bar of the City of New York, March 19, 1968. New
   York: Association of the Bar of the City of New
   York, 1968.   W 3–15

SHAKESPEARE, WILLIAM
The Complete Works of William Shakespeare . . . .
   v. 5 of 9. London and New York: Henry Frowder, Oxford University Press, 1911.   H 7–18

The Complete Works of William Shakespeare.
   Cambridge edition. Philadelphia: Blakiston Co., 1944.   RR

Hamlet: A Television Script.
   Adapted by Michael Benthall and Ralph Nelson for presentation on
   the CBS Television Network by The Old Vic Company on February
   24, 1959 . . . . n.p.   I 5–2

The Plays and Poems of Shakespeare.
   Ed. A. J. Valpy. v. 4, 7, & 14. New York: F. M. Lupton
   Co., n.d. H 7–17

Shakespeare's Works.
   v.3 & 7, International edition. n.p., n.d.   G 1–12

SHALIT, GENE and GROSSMAN, LAWRENCE K.
*Somehow It Works: A Candid Portrait of the 1964 Presidential Election
by NBC News.*
   Garden City: Doubleday and Co., 1965.   BB

SHAW, BERNARD
Nine Plays with Prefaces and Notes.
   New York: Dodd, Mead and Co., 1935.   F 2–11

SHAWN, TED
Whitman: His Immortal Leaves.
   No. 23 of 500 copies. Kent, Washington: John Victor, 1948.   I 5–4

SHERWOOD, MRS. JOHN
Manners and Social Usages.
   New York: Harper and Bros., 1887.   I 6–42

SHERWOOD, ROBERT EMMET
Abe Lincoln in Illinois: A Play in Twelve Scenes.
New York and London: Charles Scribner's Sons, 1940.   I 2–23

SHEWMAKE, OSCAR L.
The Honorable George Wythe: Address Delivered Before the Wythe Law Club of the College of William and Mary . . . December 18, 1921.
n.p., 2nd printing, 1954.   I 4–9

SHIELDS, JOSEPH D.
The Life and Times of Seargent Smith Prentiss.
Philadelphia: J. B. Lippincott and Co., 1883.   G 2–21

SHMALO, NATHAN S.
An Inquiry into the Voting Behavior of Justice Black During the 1960's: A Qualitative Attempt to Explain a Bloc Phenomenon.
Senior honors thesis, University of Miami, Department of Politics and Public Affairs, May 25, 1971.   LB

SHRINER, CHARLES A.
William Paterson.
[Paterson, N.J.]: Paterson Industrial Commission, 1940.   H 3–7

SIGLER, JAY A.
Double Jeopardy: The Development of a Legal and Social Policy.
Ithaca: Cornell University Press, 1969.   Court

SIMKINS, FRANCIS BUTLER
The South: Old and New, A History, 1820–1947.
1st edition, A Borzoi Book. New York: Alfred A. Knopf, 1947.   G 6–7

SIMMS, WILLIAM GILMORE
War Poetry of the South.
New York: Richardson and Co., 1866.   G 6–8

SINDLER, ALLAN P., ed.
Change in the Contemporary South.
Durham: Duke University Press, 1963.   W 4–2
inscribed by John P. Frank, Christmas 1963.

SKAGGS, WILLIAM H.
The Southern Oligarchy: An Appeal in Behalf of the Silent Masses of Our Country Against the Despotic Rule of the Few.
   New York: Devin-Adair Co., 1924.   G 6–6
   marked.

SLOSS, EDITH TYNDALE
Echoes of the Old Plantation.
   Contemporary Poets of Dorrance (330). Philadelphia: Dorrance and Co., 1947.   G 6–21
   inscribed by the author, n.d.

SLOSSON, PRESTON WILLIAM
The Great Crusade and After, 1914–1928.
   New York: Macmillan Co., 1930.   I 4–14
   marked, FSL.

SMITH, A. DELAFIELD
The Right to Life.
   Chapel Hill: University of North Carolina Press, 1955.   Court

SMITH, BERNARD, ed.
The Democratic Spirit: A Collection of American Writings from the Earliest Times to the Present Day.
   New York: Alfred A. Knopf, 1941.   I 3–10
   marked, FSL.

SMITH, DARRELL HEVENOR
. . . The Forest Service: Its History, Activities, and Organization . . . .
   Washington, D.C.: Brookings Institution, 1930.   Court

SMITH, JAMES BARCLAY
Studies in the Adequacy of the Constitution.
   Los Angeles: Parker and Baird, 1939.   RR

SMITH, JOHN E., ed.
Contemporary American Philosophy.
   2nd series, Muirhead Library of Philosophy. New York: Humanities Press, 1970.   LB

SMITH, JOSEPH, JR., tr.
The Book of Mormon.
 Salt Lake City: Church of Jesus Christ of Latter Day
 Saints, 1961.   I 6–25

SPENCER, CLARISSA YOUNG with HARMER, MABEL
Brigham Young at Home.
 Salt Lake City: Desert Book Co., 1963.   LA

SPENCER, HAZELTON
The Art and Life of William Shakespeare.
 New York: Harcourt, Brace and Co., 1940.   H 7–6
 heavily marked.

SPINOZA, BENEDICTUS DE
Improvement of the Understanding, Ethics, and Correspondence.
 Tr. R. H. M. Elwes. New York: Willey Book Co., 1901.   F 4–12

SQUIRE, ANNE
Social Washington.
 Washington, D.C.: Byron S. Adams Press, 1923.   I 6–18

STANLEY, ARTHUR PENRHYN
Historical Memorials of Westminster Abbey.
 2 v. London: J. Murray, n.d.   RR

STEWART, GEORGE R.
The Year of the Oath: The Fight for Academic Freedom at the University of California.
 Garden City: Doubleday and Co., 1950.   I 3–20
 FSL.

STIRLING, SARAH VOWELL DAINGERFIELD
Thoughts.
 2nd edition. New York: Poets Press, 1940.   G 5–16
 inscribed by the author, n.d.

STOURZH, GERALD and LERNER, RALPH, eds.
Readings in American Democracy.
   2 v., 1st edition, revised. Chicago: American Foundation for Political
   Education, 1958.
   v. 1   Court
   v. 2   I 2–27

STRICKLAND, STEPHEN PARKS, ed.
Hugo Black and the Supreme Court.
   Indianapolis: Bobbs-Merrill Co., [1967].   w 3–6

STRODE, HUDSON
Finland Forever.
   1st edition. New York: Harcourt, Brace and Co., 1941.   G 7–14
   marked, personally indexed.
   inscribed by the author, n.d.

Jefferson Davis: Confederate President.
   1st edition. New York: Harcourt Brace and Co., 1959.

The Story of Bermuda.
   New York: Harrison Smith and Robert Haas, 1932.   G 7–31
   inscribed by the author, September 1933.

Timeless Mexico.
   New York: Harcourt, Brace and Co., 1944.   G 7–32
   marked.
   inscribed by the author, n.d.

STRUNK, WILLIAM, JR. and WHITE, E. B.
The Elements of Style.
   New York: Macmillan Co., n.d.   w 2–42
   inscribed by Chuck Luce, January 19, 1962.

STRYKER, LLOYD PAUL
Andrew Johnson: A Study in Courage.
   New York: Macmillan Co., 1930.   G 3–12

The Art of Advocacy: A Plea for the Renaissance of the Trial Lawyer.
   New York: Simon and Schuster, 1954.   I 2–26
   inscribed by the author, March 11, 1954.

[STRYKER, LLOYD PAUL, *cont.*]
For the Defense: Thomas Erskine, the Most Enlightened Liberal of His Times, 1750–1823.
  1st edition. Garden City: Doubleday and Co., 1947. H 3–29
  marked, personally indexed.
  inscribed by the author, June 5, 1947.

SUETONIUS [C. SUETONIUS TRANQUILLUS]
The Lives of the Twelve Caesars.
  Tr. Alexander Thomson. revised and corrected. New York: R. Worthington, 1883. H 5–2
  marked, personally indexed.

SULLIVAN, ALOYSIUS MICHAEL
The Bottom of the Sea.
  New York: Dun and Bradstreet, 1966.   Court

SUMNER, G. LYNN
Meet Abraham Lincoln: Profiles of the Prairie President.
  Chicago: printed for Abraham Lincoln Book Shop, 1946.   G 4–20
  inscribed by the author, February 3, 1946.

SUTHERLAND, ARTHUR E.
Apology for Uncomfortable Change, 1865–1965.
  New York: Macmillan Co., [1965].   Court

SUTHERLAND, ARTHUR E., ed.
Government Under Law: Conference Held at Harvard Law School on the Occasion of the Bicentennial of John Marshall, Chief Justice of the United States, 1801–1835.
  Cambridge, Mass.: Harvard University Press, 1956.   W 4–8

SUTHERLAND, GEORGE
Proceedings in the U.S. Supreme Court in Memory of George Sutherland, December 18, 1944.
  Washington, D.C.: U.S. Government Printing Office, 1944. H 3–35

SWISHER, CARL BRENT
American Constitutional Development.
  Boston and New York: Houghton Mifflin Co., [1943].   CL B 2–29

[SWISHER, CARL BRENT, *cont.*]
The Growth of Constitutional Power in the United States.
   Chicago: University of Chicago Press, [1946].   Court
   marked.
   inscribed by the author, n.d.

Stephen J. Field
   Washington, D.C.: Brookings Institution, 1930.   B 1–1

SYRACUSE UNIVERSITY: MAXWELL GRADUATE
SCHOOL OF CITIZENSHIP and PUBLIC AFFAIRS
*The Three Syracuses and the Three-P Professorship: Being Syntheses
of Poetry, Politics, and Philosophy as Disclosed on T. V. Smith Day,
Syracuse University, November 10, 1948.*
   published by the author.   1 5–5

TACITUS, CORNELIUS
The Works of Cornelius Tacitus . . . .
   Ed. Arthur Murphy. 2 v. London: printed by W. Green and T. Chap-
   lin for J. Davis, Military Chronicle Office, 1813.   F 3–2
   v. 2 personally indexed.

The Works of Tacitus: The Annals.
   2 v., Oxford translation, revised. New York: Harper and
   Bros., 1871.   W 2–13
   heavily marked.

TAGORE, RABINDRANATH
The Gardener.
   New York: Macmillan Co., 1934.   1 5–33

TALBERT, WILLIAM F.
Tennis Observed: Photos and Stories About Early Tennis Players.
   Barre, Mass.: Barre Publishers, 1967.   BB

TANSILL, CHARLES CULLAN, ed.
*Documents Illustrative of the Formation of the Union of the American
States.*
   H. R. Doc. No. 398, 69th Cong., 1st Sess. (1927).   CL B–14
   marked, personally indexed.

TAYLOR, A[LFRED] E[DWARD]
Socrates: The Man and His Thoughts.
  A Doubleday Anchor Book. Garden City: Doubleday and
  Co., 1954.   W 1–41
  heavily marked.

TAYLOR, HANNIS
Due Process of Law and Equal Protection.
  Chicago: Callaghan and Co., 1917.   CL B 2–10
  marked.

TAYLOR, JOHN METCALF
The Witchcraft Delusion in Colonial Connecticut, 1647–1697.
  New York: Grafton Press, [1908].   W 2–30

TAYLOR, TELFORD
Nuremberg and Vietnam: An American Tragedy.
  A New York Times Book. Chicago: Quadrangle
  Books, 1970.   W 2–34

TEILHARD DE CHARDIN, PIERRE
The Phenomenon of Man.
  New York: Harper and Bros., [1959].   Court
  marked.

TERENCE
The Comedies of Terence.
  Trs. Henry Thomas Riley and George Colman. New York: Harper
  and Bros., 1892.   F 2–10

THANE, ELSWYTH
Potomac Squire.
  New York: Duell, Sloan and Pearce, 1963.   BB

THOMAS, BENJAMIN P.
Abraham Lincoln: A Biography.
  A Borzoi Book. New York: Alfred A. Knopf, 1952.   G 4–19
  heavily marked, personally indexed.
  inscribed by John Frank, Christmas 1953.

THOMAS, ELBERT D.
The Four Fears.
   Chicago and New York: Ziff-Davis Publishing Co., 1944.   I 5–16

THORNDIKE, ASHLEY H., ed.
Modern Eloquence.
   2 v. New York: Modern Eloquence Corp., 1923.   BB

THUCYDIDES
The Peloponnesian War.
   Tr. Crawley. 1st Modern Library edition, The Complete Writings of
   Thucydides. New York: Modern Library (Random
   House), 1934.   F 2–19.

Thucydides, Translated into English.
   Tr. Benjamin Jowett, revisors W. H. Forbes and Evelyn Abbott. 2 v.,
   2nd edition, revised. Oxford: Clarendon Press, 1900.   F 1–14
   v. 1 marked, personally indexed.

TILLEY, JOHN S.
Facts the Historians Leave Out.
   Montgomery, Ala.: Paragon Press, 5th printing, 1953.   G 7–35
   inscribed by the author, n.d.

DE TOCQUEVILLE, ALEXIS
Democracy in America.
   Tr. Henry Reeve. 2 v., revised edition, World's Great Classics. New
   York: Colonial Press, 1899.   F 4–7
   marked, personally indexed.

TODD, A[LDEN] L.
Justice on Trial: The Case of Louis D. Brandeis.
   New York, Toronto, and London: McGraw Hill Book
   Co., 1964.   CL B 2–8
   marked.

TOLSTOY, LEO
War and Peace.
   Trs. Louise and Aylmer Maude. Inner Sanctum edition. New York:
   Simon and Schuster, 1942.   H 6–3

TOUHY, ROGER with BRENNAN, RAY
The Stolen Years.
   Cleveland: Pennington Press, 1959.   H 6–9
   inscribed by Ray Brennan, October 26, 1959.

TOYNBEE, ARNOLD J.
Greek Civilization and Character.
   A Mentor Book. New York: New American Library, 1953.   F 5–22
   marked, personally indexed.

another copy.   W 2–22

A Study of History.
   v. 1, 9, & 10. New York and London: Oxford Press, 1947.   G 1–19
   v. 1 marked, personally indexed.

TRAYNOR, ROGER J.
The Devils of Due Process in Criminal Detection, Detention, and Trial.
   23rd Annual Benjamin N. Cardozo Lecture, delivered before the Association of the Bar of the City of New York, April 19, 1966. New
   York: New York City Bar Association, 1966.   H 7–11

TREVELYAN, G[EORGE] M[ACAULAY]
The Tudors and the Stuart Era.
   v. 2 of History of England. A Doubleday Anchor Book. Garden City:
   Doubleday and Co., 1953.   W 1–40
   heavily marked.

TREVELYAN, GEORGE OTTO
The Early History of Charles James Fox.
   New York: Harper and Bros., 1881.   G 3–7

TROLLOPE, ANTHONY
North America.
   Eds. Donald Smalley and Bradford Allen Booth. A Borzoi Book. New
   York: Alfred A. Knopf, 1951.   G 1–5
   marked.

TRUMAN, HARRY S
Mr. Citizen.
   Author's edition. [New York]: Bernard Geis Associates, distributed
   by Random House, [1960].   RR
   inscribed by the author, September 22, 1960.

TULLY, GRACE
F.D.R.: My Boss.
  New York: Charles Scribner's Sons, 1949.   Court

TYLER, JOHN and 18 Others
A Selection of Eulogies in Honor of Those Illustrious Patriots and Statesmen, John Adams and Thomas Jefferson.
  Hartford, Conn.: D. F. Robinson and Co. and Norton and Russell,
  1826.   G 2–18
  marked.

UNDERWOOD, OSCAR W.
Drifting Sands of Party Politics.
  Special memorial edition. New York and London: Century
  Co., 1931.   G 7–18

U.S. COMMISSION ON CIVIL RIGHTS
Report.
  Washington, D.C.: U.S. Government Printing Office, 1959.   Court

U.S. CONGRESS
Debates on the Judiciary . . . During the First Session of the Seventh Congress . . . .
  Albany: printed by Whiting, Leavenworth and
  Whiting, 1802.   Court
  marked, personally indexed.

U.S. CONGRESS: HOUSE OF REPRESENTATIVES
Proceedings at the Ceremonies in Commemoration of the 150th Anniversary of the First Meeting of the Supreme Court of the United States.
  H. Doc. No. 649, 76th Cong., 3rd Sess. (1940).   B 1–10

U.S. CONGRESS: SENATE COMMITTEE ON FOREIGN RELATIONS
State Department Employee Loyalty Investigation and Part 2, Individual Views of Senator Lodge.
  S. Rep't No. 2108, 81st Cong., 2nd Sess. (1950).   G 7–24

State Department Employee Loyalty Investigation: Hearings Before a Subcommittee.
  U.S. Senate, 81st Cong., 2nd Sess. (1950), pursuant to S. Res. 231.
  Part 3, June 28, 1950.   I 4–33

U.S. Congress: Special Senate Committee on Investigation
of Air Mail and Ocean Mail Contracts
Hearings, 73rd Cong., pursuant to S. Res. 349, 72nd Cong. Part 4, January 9 to January 18, 1934.
Washington, D.C.: U.S. Government Printing
Office, 1934.   w 4–33

U.S. Constitution Sesquicentennial Commission
The Story of the Constitution, 1787–1937.
Washington, D.C.: U.S. Constitution Sesquicentennial Commission,
1937.   w 4–12

U.S. Constitutional Convention, 1787
Secret Proceedings and Debates of the Federal Convention Assembled at Philadelphia in the Year 1787, For the Purpose of Forming the Constitution of the United States of America: From Notes Taken by Robert Yates, et al.
Cincinnati: Alston Mygatt, [1838].   cl b 2–16
heavily marked, personally indexed.

U.S. Department of Commerce and Labor:
Bureau of the Census
Heads of Families: First Census of the United States, 1790, State of South Carolina.
Washington, D.C.: U.S. Government Printing Office, 1908.   w 4–4

U.S. National Advisory Commission on Civil Disorders
Supplemental Studies.
Washington, D.C.: U.S. Government Printing
Office, 1968.   Court

U.S. National Commission on Reform of
Federal Criminal Laws
Working Papers . . . .
2 v. Washington, D.C.: U.S. Government Printing
Office, 1970.   Court

U.S. President's Water Policy Commission
. . . Water Resources Law: The Report of the President.
v. 3. Washington, D.C.: U.S. Government Printing
Office, 1950.   Court

VAN DOREN, CARL
Benjamin Franklin.
   1st edition after publication of limited signed edition. New York:
   Viking Press, 1938.   G 2–25
   marked, personally indexed.

VAN LOON, HENDRIK WILLEM
The Story of Mankind.
   A Star Book. Garden City: Garden City Publishing
   Co., 1926.   H 6–8
   marked.

Van Loon's Lives.
   New York: Simon and Schuster, 3rd printing, 1942.   BB

VEBLEN, THORSTEIN
Imperial Germany and the Industrial Revolution.
   New York: Viking Press, 1946.   F 5–17
   marked.

The Theory of the Leisure Class.
   A Mentor Book. New York: Viking Press, 1953.   W 4–21

VINES, ELLSWORTH
How to Play Better Tennis.
   Philadelphia: David McKay Co., [1938].   W 1–4
   marked.

[VINING], ELIZABETH JANET GRAY
Anthology With Comments.
   3rd edition, Pendle Hill Pamphlet No. 18. Wallingford, Pa.: Pendle
   Hill, 1942.   I 6–34

VINOGRADOFF, PAUL
Common Sense in Law.
   London: Williams and Norgate, 1st impression, 1920.   W 4–22

VIRGINIA COMMISSION ON CONSTITUTIONAL GOVERNMENT, comp.
We The States: An Anthology of Historic Documents and Commentaries Thereon, Expounding the State and Federal Relationships.
   Richmond, Va.: William Byrd Press, 1964.   CL B 2–1

VOLTAIRE
Voltaire's Philosophical Dictionary.
   10 v. Paris, London, New York, and Chicago: E. R.
   DuMont, 1901.   F 8–1

WALFORD, EDWARD
Juvenal.
   Ancient Classics for English Readers. Edinburgh and London: William Blackwood and Sons, 1876.   F 3–12
   inscribed by Buddy Cleveland, August 8, 1953.

WALKER, ANNE KENDRICK
Braxton Bragg Comer: His Family Tree From Virginia's Colonial Days.
   Richmond, Va.: Dietz Press, 1947.   I 6–21

WALSH, WILLIAM S., comp.
International Encyclopedia of Prose and Poetical Quotations.
   Philadelphia: John C. Winston Co., 1908.   G 3–8
   marked.

WALTER, WILLIAM WILFRED, ed.
The Unknown God.
   v. 1. Aurora, Ill.: William W. Walter, 1914.   I 5–32

WARNER, REX
Pericles the Athenian.
   An Atlantic Monthly Press Book. Boston and Toronto: Little, Brown and Co., 1963.   F 5–28

WARREN, CHARLES
The Supreme Court in United States History.
   Revised edition. 2 v. Boston: Little, Brown and Co., 1937.
   marked.

WARREN, EARL
Address Delivered at the 46th Annual Meeting of the American Law Institute, May 20, 1969.
   [Philadelphia, 1969].   B 1–15

[WARREN, EARL, *cont.*]
Hughes and the Court.
   Hamilton, N.Y.: Colgate University Press, 1962.   B 1–8

The Public Papers of Chief Justice Earl Warren.
   Ed. Henry M. Christman. New York: Simon and Schuster, 1st printing, 1959.   H 3–23

WATSON, THOMAS E.
The Life and Times of Andrew Jackson.
   Thomson, Ga.: Jeffersonian Publishing Co., 1917.   G 4–7

The Life and Times of Thomas Jefferson.
   Thomson, Ga.: Jeffersonian Publishing Co., 1918.   G 4–11
   marked, personally indexed.

Napoleon: A Sketch of His Life, Character, Struggles and Achievements.
   Thomson, Ga.: Jeffersonian Publishing Co., 1920.   G 2–23

The Story of France, From the Earliest Times to the Consulate of Napoleon Bonaparte.
   2 v., 7th edition. Thomson, Ga.: Jeffersonian Publishing Co.,
   1919.   G 2–24
   v. 1 marked.
   v. 2 personally indexed.

WATSON, THOMAS J.
Unconquerable: A Review of the Historic Visit to the United States and Canada Which Was Made During June and July, 1942, by His Majesty Peter II, King of Yugoslavia.
   n.p., 1942.   G 7–27

WEBB, WALTER PRESCOTT
Divided We Stand: The Crisis of a Frontierless Democracy.
   New York and Toronto: Farrar and Rinehart, 1937.   G 6–18

WEBSTER, DANIEL
Works.
   6 v., 17th edition. Boston: Little, Brown and Co., 1877.   G 1–7

WEBSTER, NOAH
Webster's New International Dictionary.
   Ed. W. T. Harris. Springfield, Mass.: G. and C. Merriam
   Co., 1914.   CL B–13

WEEKS, STEPHEN B.
History of Public School Education in Alabama.
U.S. Bureau of Education Bulletin, 1915, No. 12. Washington, D.C.:
U.S. Government Printing Office, 1915.   G 6–17
marked.

WELLS, H[ERBERT] G[EORGE]
The Outline of History.
v. 1. New York: Macmillan Co., 1921.   F 1–15

The Rights of Man, or, What Are We Fighting For?
Harmondsworth, Middlesex, Eng., and New York: Penguin Books,
[1940].   W 2–28

WENDT, LLOYD and KOGAN, HERMAN
Big Bill of Chicago.
1st edition. Indianapolis and New York: Bobbs-Merrill
Co., 1953.   I 6–16
inscribed by Herman Kogan, n.d.

WERTENBAKER, THOMAS JEFFERSON
The Puritan Oligarchy: The Founding of American Civilization.
New York and London: Charles Scribner's Sons, 1947.   I 2–17
heavily marked, personally indexed.

WEST, HERBERT FAULKNER
Rebel Thought.
Boston: Beacon Press, 1953.   CL B 2–15

WESTIN, ALAN F.
*The Anatomy of a Constitutional Law Case: Youngstown Sheet and
Tube Co. v. Sawyer, the Steel Seizure Decision.*
New York: Macmillan Co., 1st printing, 1958.   I 3–19

Privacy and Freedom.
New York: Atheneum, 1967.   Court

WESTIN, ALAN F., ed.
*An Autobiography of the Supreme Court: Speeches, Letters, Memoirs
of Justices, 1790–1961.*
New York: Macmillan Co., [1963].   W 4–25

WEYL, NATHANIEL
The Battle Against Disloyalty.
New York: Thomas Y. Crowell Co., 1951.   I 3–28
FSL.

WHEELER, JOSEPH
Proceedings in Statuary Hall of the United States Capitol upon the Unveiling and Presentation of the Statue of General Joseph Wheeler by the State of Alabama.
H. Doc. No. 480, 69th Cong., 1st Sess. (1926).   G 4–16

WHIPPLE, LEON
Our Ancient Liberties: The Story of the Origin and Meaning of Civil and Religious Liberty in the United States.
New York: H. W. Wilson Co., 1927.   CL B–10

WHISNANT, CHARLEEN
Red Clay Reader.
Charlotte, N.C.: Southern Review, 1964.   W 3–37

WHITE, THEODORE
The Making of the President, 1964.
A Signet Book. New York: New American Library, 1st printing, 1966.   I 6–44

WHITEHEAD, ALFRED NORTH
The Aims of Education.
A Mentor Book. New York: Macmillan Co., 1929.   W 1–45
heavily marked.

Essays in Science and Philosophy.
New York: Philosophical Library, 1948.   CL B 2–14
marked.

WHITLOCK, BRAND
La Fayette.
New York and London: D. Appleton and Co., 1929.   Court

WILLIAM and MARY COLLEGE
Marshall, Wythe, Blackstone Commemoration Ceremonies, College of William and Mary, Saturday, September 25, 1954.
Williamsburg: privately printed, 1954.   W 1–29
inscribed by Alvin Duke Chandler, n.d.

WILLIAMS, CHARLOTTE
Hugo Black.
    Baltimore: Johns Hopkins Press, 1950.   w 3–3

another copy.   w 3–4

WILLIAMS, GLANVILLE
The Sanctity of Life and the Criminal Law.
    New York: Alfred A. Knopf, 1957.   Court
    marked.

WILLIAMS, T. HARRY
Huey Long.
    New York: Alfred A. Knopf, 1969.   I 7–9
    inscribed by Chuck and Helen Luce, Christmas 1969.

WILSON, EPIPHANIUS, ed.
Oriental Literature.
    v. 4 of World's Great Classics. New York: Colonial
    Press, 1899.   G 6–3

WILSON, ERNEST C.
Every Good Desire.
    Los Angeles: Unity Classics, 1948.   I 4–22

WILSON, WOODROW
Cabinet Government in the United States.
    Limited edition for Woodrow Wilson Foundation. Stamford, Conn.:
    Overbrook Press, 1947.   G 6–16

A History of the American People.
    5 v. New York: William H. Wise and Co., 1931.
    v. 3 marked, personally indexed.   H 7–4
    v. 1, 2, 4 & 5   RR

WIRT, WILLIAM
Sketches of the Life and Character of Patrick Henry.
    Revised edition. Ithaca, N.Y.: Andrus, Gauntlett and
    Co., 1850.   G 4–17
    marked.

WOLLSTONECRAFT, MARY
The Rights of Woman.
   Every Man's Library, No. 825. London: J. M. Dent and Sons; New
   York: E. P. Dutton and Co., 1929.   w 2–24

WOOD, HARRY
Lew Davis: Twenty-Five Years of Painting in Arizona.
   Arizona State University and Phoenix Art Museum, 1961.   H 7–2
   inscribed by Lew Davis, n.d.

WOODWARD, C. VANN
Origins of the New South, 1877–1913.
   v. 9 of Wendell Holmes Stephenson and E. Merton Coulter: A History of the South. Baton Rouge: Louisiana State University Press,
   1951.   G 5–33

The South in Search of a Philosophy.
   Phi Beta Kappa Address Delivered at University of Florida, December 1938. Phi Beta Kappa Series No. I. Gainesville: University of
   Florida, 1938.   G 6–13
   inscribed by the author, n.d.

WOODWARD, W[ILLIAM] E.
A New American History.
   New York: Garden City Publishing Co., 1938.   G 7–16

World Geographic Atlas: A Composite of Man's Environment.
   Ed. Herbert Boyer. privately printed for Container Corp. of America, 1953.   w 3–33

WYZANSKI, CHARLES E., JR.
Whereas, A Judge's Premises: Essays in Judgment, Ethics, and the Law.
   An Atlantic Monthly Press Book. Boston: Little, Brown and Co.,
   1964.   CL B 2–25
   heavily marked, personally indexed.

YEATS, WILLIAM BUTLER
The Collected Poems of W. B. Yeats.
   New York: Macmillan Co., 1938.   I 2–5

Wheels and Butterflies.
   New York: Macmillan Co., 1935.   I 5–15

YERBY, WILLIAM EDWARD WADSWORTH
History of Greensboro, Alabama, From its Earliest Settlement.
Montgomery, Ala.: Paragon Press, 1908.   G 5–27
inscribed by Mrs. H. M. Beck, n.d.

ZIMMERN, ALFRED
The Greek Commonwealth: Politics and Economics in Fifth Century Athens.
5th edition, revised. Oxford: Clarendon Press, 1931.   F 5–8
heavily marked, personally indexed.

ZUNDER, THEODORE ALBERT
The Early Days of Joel Barlow: A Connecticut Wit.
v. 84 of Yale Studies in English. New Haven: Yale University Press, 1934.   I 2–15

Subject Listings

Every book listed in the preceding alphabetical catalogue is listed under at least one of the nineteen subject headings below. No book appears under more than two headings. In examining these lists, allowance must be made for the usual difficulties in classifying books. Though broad, the categories should be sufficiently meaningful to afford insight into the composition of Mr. Justice Black's personal library.

Alabama
American Biography and History
American Law
Hugo L. Black
Contemporary Affairs
English History, Biography, and Law
English Literature
European History, Biography, and Law
Fiction
Greece
Thomas Jefferson
Miscellaneous
Philosophy, Jurisprudence, and Religion
Poetry
Reference Works
Rome
The South
Tennis
World History

Only the author and title of each book are included. For fuller information, the listing of the book in the alphabetical catalogue should be consulted.

ALABAMA

Abernethy, Thomas Perkins. *The Formative Period in Alabama, 1815–1828*.

Alabama Historical Society. *Transactions*.

Arnold, Byron, comp. *Folksongs of Alabama*.

Avery, Mary Johnston. *She Heard with Her Heart: Life of Mrs. R. D. Johnston, Founder and Guiding Spirit of Alabama Boys' Industrial School*.

Blakely, Hunter B. *Religion in Shoes: Brother Bryan of Birmingham*. 2 copies.

Bonner, Clint. *How They Got There*.

Boyd, Minnie Clare. *Alabama in the Fifties: A Social Study*.

Brantley, William H. *Chief Justice Stone of Alabama*.

Brewer, Willis. *Alabama: Her History, Resources, War Record, and Public Men From 1540 to 1872*.

Brown, Virginia Pounds and Nabers, Jane Porter, eds. *Mary Gordon Duffee's Sketches of Alabama: Being an Account of the Journey from Tuscaloosa to Blount Springs Through Jefferson County on the Old Stage Roads*.

Carmer, Carl. *Stars Fell on Alabama*.

Ceremonies Attending the Sesquicentennial of the Battle of Horseshoe Bend and Dedication of the Park Visitor Center, Friday, March 27, 1964, 2 p.m.

Clark, John B[unyan]. *Populism in Alabama*. 2 copies.

Comings, L. J. Newcomb and Albers, Martha M. *A Brief History of Baldwin County*.

The Corolla. v. 13 (1905) and v. 23 (1916).

Crittenden, H[enry] H[uston], comp. *The Crittenden Memoirs*.

Davis, Posey Oliver. *One Man: Edward Asbury O'Neal, III, of Alabama*.

DuBose, Joel Campbell. *Alabama History*.

——, ed. *Notable Men of Alabama, Personal and Genealogical, With Portraits*.

Fleming, Walter L. *Civil War and Reconstruction in Alabama*. 2 copies.

Garrett, William. *Reminiscences of Public Men in Alabama for Thirty Years*.

Hamilton, Peter J. *Colonial Mobile: An Historical Study, Largely From Original Sources . . . .*

Henley, John C., Jr. *This is Birmingham: The Story of the Founding and Growth of an American City*.

Hill, Henrietta McCormick. *The Family Skeleton: A History and Genalogy [sic] of the Flewellen, Fontaine, Copeland, Treutlen, McCormick, Allan and Stuart Families*.

Holloway, William Vernon and Smith, Charles W., Jr. *Government and Politics in Alabama*.

[Hooper, Johnson Jones]. *Adventures of Captain Simon Suggs, Late of the Tallapoosa Volunteers, Together with "Taking the Census," and Other Alabama Sketches.*

King, Martin Luther, Jr. *Stride Toward Freedom: The Montgomery Story.*

McCorvey, Thomas Chalmers. *Alabama Historical Poems.*

National League of American Pen Women, Alabama Members. *Historic Homes of Alabama and Their Traditions.*

Owen, Marie Bankhead, comp. *Our State: Alabama.*

Owen, Thomas McAdory. *History of Alabama and Dictionary of Alabama Biography.*

Pickett, Albert James. *History of Alabama, and Incidentally of Georgia and Mississippi, From the Earliest Period.*

Pioneers Club. *Early Days in Birmingham: A Printing of the Original Papers of the Pioneers Club Whose Members Were Eye-Witnesses to the Events of the Founding of the City.*

Riley, Benjamin Franklin. *History of the Baptists of Alabama: From the Time of Their First Occupation of Alabama in 1808 Until 1894 . . . .*

——. *A Memorial History of the Baptists of Alabama . . . .*

Seay, B[urwell] W[arren], IV. *Descendants of Abraham Seay and Seay Miscellany.*

Walker, Anne Kendrick. *Braxton Bragg Comer: His Family Tree From Virginia's Colonial Days.*

Weeks, Stephen B. *History of Public School Education in Alabama.*

Wheeler, Joseph. *Proceedings in Statuary Hall of the United States Capitol upon the Unveiling and Presentation of the Statue of General Joseph Wheeler by the State of Alabama.*

Yerby, William Edward Wadsworth. *History of Greensboro, Alabama, From its Earliest Settlement.*

AMERICAN BIOGRAPHY AND HISTORY

Adams, Charles Francis. *An Autobiography (1835–1915).*

Adams, Henry. *The Education of Henry Adams: An Autobiography.*

Adams, James Truslow. *The Epic of America.* 2 copies.

——. *The Living Jefferson.*

Adams, John. *A Defence of the Constitutions of Government of the United States of America.*

——. *Diary and Autobiography of John Adams.*

Adams, John Quincy. *Letters of John Quincy Adams to Edward Livingston.*

Alderman, Edwin Anderson and Gordon, Armistead Churchill. *J. L. M. Curry: A Biography*.

Ames, Fisher. *Works of Fisher Ames: Compiled by a Number of His Friends to Which are Prefixed Notices of His Life and Character*.

Analectic Magazine: May 1814.

Arnold, Thurman Wesley. *Fair Fights and Foul: A Dissenting Lawyer's Life*.

Baker, Edward Dickinson. *Masterpieces of E. D. Baker*.

Baker, Liva. *Felix Frankfurter*.

Bancroft, George. *History of the Formation of the Constitution of the United States of America*.

———. *History of the United States of America*.

Barnard, Harry. *Eagle Forgotten: The Life of John Peter Altgeld*.

Barth, Alan. *Heritage of Liberty*.

Beard, Charles A. *The Republic: Conversations on Fundamentals*.

———, and Mary R. *America in Midpassage*.

———. *The American Spirit*.

———. *A Basic History of the United States*.

———. *The Rise of American Civilization*.

Bemis, Samuel Flagg. *John Quincy Adams and the Union*.

Benton, Thomas H. *Thirty Years' View, or, A History of the Working of the American Government for Thirty Years From 1820–1850*.

———. *Thirty Years in the United States Senate*.

Beveridge, Albert J. *The Life of John Marshall*.

Biddle, Francis. *Mr. Justice Holmes*.

Bigelow, John. *The Life of Samuel J. Tilden*.

Bingham, John Armor. *Trial of the Conspirators for the Assassination of President Lincoln and Company*.

Bishop, Cortland F. *History of Elections in the American Colonies*.

Black, Hugo L. (See Hugo L. Black)

Blakely, Hunter B. *Religion in Shoes: Brother Bryan of Birmingham*. 2 copies.

Blunt, Wilfred. *Cockerell: A Life of Sydney Carlyle Cockerell (1867–1962)*.

Bowen, Catherine Drinker. *John Adams and the American Revolution*.

———. *Miracle at Philadelphia: The Story of the Constitutional Convention, May to September 1787*.

Bowers, Claude G. *My Life: The Memoirs of Claude Bowers*.

———. *The Tragic Era: The Revolution After Lincoln*. 3 copies

Brandeis, Louis Dembitz. *Urban Reformer: 1870–1907*.

Brandon, Leroy D., comp. *Platforms of the Two Great Political Parties: 1932 to 1940*.

Brennan, William J. *Proceedings in Honor of Mr. Justice Brennan*.

Brigham, Johnson. *James Harlan.*

Brooks, Aubrey Lee. *Walter Clark: Fighting Judge.*

Brooks, Van Wyck. *Literature in New England: The Flowering of New England, 1815–1865. New England: Indian Summer, 1865–1915.*

——. *The World of Washington Irving.*

Bryce, James. *The American Commonwealth.*

Burton, Harold H. *Memorial Publication of the Bar and Officers of the Supreme Court of the United States.*

Busch, Noel F. *Adlai E. Stevenson of Illinois.*

Butler, Pierce. *Proceedings in the U.S. Supreme Court in Memory of Pierce Butler, January 27, 1940.*

Butts, R. Freeman. *The American Tradition in Religion and Education.*

Cardozo, Benjamin N. *Proceedings in the U.S. Supreme Court in Memory of Benjamin Nathan Cardozo, November 26, 1938.*

Carter, Richard. *Breakthrough: The Saga of Jonas Salk.*

Chafee, Zechariah, Jr. *The Blessings of Liberty.*

Claiborne, J[ohn] F[rancis] H[amtramck]. *Life and Correspondence of John A. Quitman, Major-General, U.S.A., and Governor of the State of Mississippi.*

Clay, Henry. *The Life and Speeches of Henry Clay.*

Cleveland, Grover. *Letters of Grover Cleveland: 1850–1908.*

Commager, Henry Steele, ed. *Documents of American History.*

Curti, Merle. *The Roots of American Loyalty.*

Donald, David. *Charles Sumner and the Coming of the Civil War.*

——. *Lincoln's Herndon.*

Dorfman, Joseph. *The Economic Mind in American Civilization.*

—— and Tugwell, R. G. *Early American Policy: Six Columbia Contributors.*

Draper, John William. *History of the American Civil War.*

DuBose, John Witherspoon. *The Life and Times of William Lowndes Yancey.*

Dykeman, Wilma and Stokely, James. *Seeds of Southern Change: The Life of Will Alexander.*

Edmonds, George. *Facts and Falsehoods Concerning the War on the South, 1861–1865.*

Fairman, Charles. *Mr. Justice Miller and the Supreme Court, 1862–1890.*

Farley, James A. *Jim Farley's Story: The Roosevelt Years.*

The Federalist: A Collection of Essays by Alexander Hamilton, John Jay, and James Madison, Interpreting the Constitution of the United States as Agreed Upon by the Federal Convention, September 17, 1787.

Fiske, John. *The Critical Period of American History, 1783–1789.*

Frank, Jerome. *Save America First.*

Frank, John P. *Justice Daniel Dissenting: A Biography of Peter V. Daniel, 1784–1860.*

——. *Lincoln as a Lawyer.* 2 copies.

Frankfurter, Felix. *Proceedings of the Bar and Officers of the Supreme Court of the United States, October 25, 1965, in Memory of Felix Frankfurter.*

Franklin, Benjamin. *The Papers of Benjamin Franklin.*

——. *Works of the Late Dr. Benjamin Franklin, Consisting of His Life, Written by Himself, Together With Essays, Humorous, Moral, and Literary, Chiefly in the Manner of the Spectator.*

Freeman, Douglas Southall. *George Washington: A Biography.*

Andrew Furseth, 1854–1938.

Gelber, Lionel. *The American Anarchy: Democracy in an Era of Bigness.*

Gerry, Elbridge, Jr. *The Diary of Elbridge Gerry, Jr.*

Golden, Harry. *Carl Sandburg.*

——. *The Right Time: An Autobiography.*

Grund, Francis Joseph. *Aristocracy in America.*

Hand, Learned. *Proceedings Commemorating Fifty Years of Federal Judicial Service by the Honorable Learned Hand.* 2 copies.

Hanley, Thomas O'Brien. *Their Rights and Liberties: The Beginnings of Religious and Political Freedom in Maryland.*

Haraszti, Zoltán. *John Adams and the Prophets of Progress.*

Harris, Joel Chandler, ed. *Life of Henry W. Grady, Including His Writings and Speeches.*

Harris, Wilmer C. *Public Life of Zachariah Chandler 1851–1875.*

Hellman, George S. *Benjamin N. Cardozo: American Judge.*

Henry, Robert Selph. *The Story of the Confederacy.*

Hill, Benjamin Harvey, Jr., comp. *Senator Benjamin H. Hill of Georgia: His Life Speeches and Writings.*

Hill, Henrietta McCormick. *The Family Skeleton: A History and Genalogy [sic] of the Flewellen, Fontaine, Copeland, Treutlen, McCormick, Allan and Stuart Families.*

Hill, Walker H., ed. *Learning and Living: Proceedings of an Anniversary Celebration in Honor of Alexander Meiklejohn, Chicago, May 8–10, 1942.*

Hilliard, Henry W. *Speeches and Addresses.*

Hoover, Herbert. *The Ordeal of Woodrow Wilson.*

Howe, Mark DeWolfe. *Justice Oliver Wendell Holmes: The Shaping Years, 1841–1870.*

Howlett, Duncan. *No Greater Love: The James Reeb Story.*

Hubbard, Elbert, comp. *Elbert Hubbard's Scrap Book: Containing the Inspired and Inspiring Selections, Gathered During a Life Time of Discriminating Reading For His Own Use.*

Hubbard, Elbert, II, comp. *The Notebook of Elbert Hubbard: Mottoes, Epigrams, Short Essays, Passages, Orphic Sayings and Preachments.*

Hunt, Gaillard. *John C. Calhoun.*

Hutcheson, Joseph C., Jr. *We March But We Remember.*

Inouye, Daniel K. with Elliott, Lawrence. *Journey to Washington.*

Jackson, Robert Houghwout. *Proceedings of the Bar and Officers of the Supreme Court of the United States, April 4, 1955, in Memory of Robert Houghwout Jackson. Washington, D.C., 1955.*

James, Marquis. *Andrew Jackson: The Border Captain.*

——. *Andrew Jackson: Portrait of a President.*

Jefferson, Thomas. (See Thomas Jefferson).

Jeffery, Reginald W. *The History of the Thirteen Colonies of North America, 1497–1763.*

Jensen, Merrill. *The New Nation: A History of the U.S. During the Confederation, 1781–1789.*

Jensen, Oliver Ormerod; Kerr, Joan Paterson; and Belsky, Murray. *American Album: Rare Photos.*

Johnson, Allen, ed. *Dictionary of American Biography.*

Johnson, Lady Bird. *A White House Diary.*

Jones, William Carey. *Illustrated History of the University of California.*

Kennedy, John F. *Profiles in Courage.*

Kennedy, John P. *Memoirs of the Life of William Wirt.*

Key, V[aldimer] O[rlando], Jr. *Southern Politics in State and Nation.*

Knopf, Alfred A. *Portrait of a Publisher, 1915–1965: Reminiscences and Reflections.*

Koch, Adrienne. *Jefferson and Madison: The Great Collaboration.*

Kogan, Herman and Wendt, Lloyd. *Chicago: A Pictorial History.*

Konefsky, Samuel J. *John Marshall and Alexander Hamilton: Architects of the American Constitution.*

LaFollette, Belle Case and Fola. *Robert M. LaFollette.*

Lehman, Irving. *Benjamin Nathan Cardozo: A Memorial.*

Lerner, Max. *America as a Civilization: Life and Thought in the United States Today.*

——. *The Unfinished Country: A Book of American Symbols.*

——, ed. *The Mind and Faith of Justice Holmes.*

Lodge, Henry Cabot. *Alexander Hamilton.*

——. *Daniel Webster.*

Long, Huey Pierce. *Memorial Services Held in the House of Representatives of the United States, Together with Remarks Presented in Eulogy of Huey Pierce Long, Late a Senator from Louisiana.*

Maclay, William. *The Journal of William Maclay, United States Senator from Pennsylvania, 1789–1791.*

Madison, Charles A. *Eminent American Jews: 1776 to the Present.*

Marshall, Thomas R. *Recollections of Thomas R. Marshall, Vice-President and Hoosier Philosopher: A Hoosier Salad.*

Mason, Alpheus Thomas. *Brandeis: A Free Man's Life.*

——. *William Howard Taft: Chief Justice.*

Mayhew, Jonathan. *A Discourse Concerning Unlimited Submission and Non-Resistance to the Higher Powers, With Some Reflections on the Resistance Made to King Charles I, and on the Anniversary of His Death . . . Delivered in a Sermon Preached in the West Meeting House in Boston, on the Lord's Day After the 30th of January, 1749–50.*

Mazzuchelli, [Samuel Charles]. *Memoirs: Historical and Edifying of a Missionary Apostolic of the Order of Saint Dominic Among Various Indian Tribes and Among the Catholics and Protestants in the United States of America.*

Meade, Robert Douthat. *Judah P. Benjamin: Confederate Statesman.*

Meyer, Agnes E. *Out of These Roots: The Autobiography of an American Woman.*

Michie, Allan A. and Ryhlick, Frank. *Dixie Demagogues.*

Miller, John C. *Crisis in Freedom: The Alien and Sedition Acts.* 2 copies.

Mizener, Arthur. *The Far Side of Paradise: A Biography of F. Scott Fitzgerald.*

Moore, Gay Montagne. *Seaport in Virginia: George Washington's Alexandria.*

Morgan, Edmund S. *The Birth of the Republic.*

Morgan, John Tyler and Pettus, Edmond Winston. *Memorial Addresses in the Senate of the United States, April 18, 1908 and in the House of Representatives, April 25, 1908.*

Morris, Richard B., ed. *Four Hundred Notable Americans.*

Neuberger, Richard L. and Kahn, Stephen B. *Integrity: The Life of George W. Norris.*

Nevins, Allan. *Grover Cleveland: A Study in Courage.*

Padover, Saul K., ed. *To Secure These Blessings: The Great Debates of the Constitutional Convention of 1787.*

Paine, Thomas. *The Writings of Thomas Paine.*

Parrington, Vernon Louis. *The Beginnings of Critical Realism in America, 1860–1920.*

——. *Main Currents in American Thought.*

Parton, James. *Life of Andrew Jackson.*

Paschal, Joel Francis. *Mr. Justice Sutherland.*

Peare, Catherine Owens. *The Louis D. Brandeis Story.*

Perry, Ralph Barton. *The Thought and Character of William James.*

Petersen, Svend, comp. *Mark Twain and the Government.*

Powell, Mary G. *The History of Old Alexandria, Virginia, From July 13, 1749 to May 24, 1861.*

Pringle, Henry R. *The Life and Times of William Howard Taft.*

Putnam, Carleton. *High Journey: A Decade in the Pilgrimage of an Air Line Pioneer.*

Richardson, James D., comp. *A Compilation of the Messages and Papers of the Presidents, 1789–1897.*

Rodell, Fred. *Fifty-Five Men: The Story of the American Constitution.*

Roosevelt, Elliott. *As He Saw It.*

Roosevelt, Franklin Delano. *Development of United States Foreign Policy: Addresses and Messages of Franklin D. Roosevelt . . . .*

——, and Pius XII. *Wartime Correspondence Between President Roosevelt and Pope Pius XII.*

Ross, Malcolm. *Death of a Yale Man.*

Rutledge, Wiley Blount. *Proceedings in the U.S. Supreme Court in Memory of Wiley Blount Rutledge, April 10, 1951.*

Salinger, Pierre and Vanocur, Sander, eds. *A Tribute to John F. Kennedy.*

Schuckers, J[acob] W. *The Life and Public Services of Salmon Portland Chase.*

Sherwood, Robert Emmet. *Abe Lincoln in Illinois: A Play in Twelve Scenes.*

Shewmake, Oscar L. *The Honorable George Wythe: Address Delivered Before the Wythe Law Club of the College of William and Mary . . . December 18, 1921.*

Schlesinger, Arthur M. *Paths to the Present.*

Schlesinger, Arthur M., Jr. *The Age of Jackson.*

Shields, Joseph D. *The Life and Times of Seargent Smith Prentiss.*

Shriner, Charles A. *William Paterson.*

Slosson, Preston William. *The Great Crusade and After 1914–1928.*

Smith, Bernard, ed. *The Democratic Spirit: A Collection of American Writings from the Earliest Times to the Present Day.*

Spencer, Clarissa Young with Harmer, Mabel. *Brigham Young at Home.*

Stourzh, Gerald and Lerner, Ralph, eds. *Readings in American Democracy.*

Strode, Hudson. *Jefferson Davis: Confederate President.*

Stryker, Lloyd Paul. *Andrew Johnson: A Study in Courage.*

Sumner, G. Lynn. *Meet Abraham Lincoln: Profiles of the Prairie President.*

Sutherland, George. *Proceedings in the U.S. Supreme Court in Memory of George Sutherland, December 18, 1944.*

Swisher, Carl Brent. *Stephen J. Field.*

Tansill, Charles Cullan, ed. *Documents Illustrative of the Formation of the Union of the American States.*

Taylor, John Metcalf. *The Witchcraft Delusion in Colonial Connecticut, 1647–1697.*

Thane, Elswyth. *Potomac Squire.*

Thomas, Benjamin P. *Abraham Lincoln: A Biography.*

Tilley, John S. *Facts the Historians Leave Out.*

de Tocqueville, Alexis. *Democracy in America.*

Trollope, Anthony. *North America.*

Tully, Grace. *F.D.R.: My Boss.*

Tyler, John and 18 Others. *A Selection of Eulogies in Honor of Those Illustrious Patriots and Statesmen, John Adams and Thomas Jefferson.*

U.S. Congress: House of Representatives. *Proceedings at the Ceremonies in Commemoration of the 150th Anniversary of the First Meeting of the Supreme Court of the United States.*

U.S. Constitution Sesquicentennial Commission. *The Story of the Constitution, 1787–1937.*

U.S. Constitutional Convention, 1787. *Secret Proceedings and Debates of the Federal Convention Assembled at Philadelphia in the Year 1787, For the Purpose of Forming the Constitution of the United States of America: From Notes Taken by Robert Yates, et al.*

U.S. Department of Commerce and Labor: Bureau of the Census. *Heads of Families: First Census of the United States, 1790, State of South Carolina.*

Van Doren, Carl. *Benjamin Franklin.*

Virginia Commission on Constitutional Government, comp. *We the States: An Anthology of Historic Documents and Commentaries Thereon, Expounding the State and Federal Relationships.*

Watson, Thomas E. *The Life and Times of Andrew Jackson.*

Webb, Walter Prescott. *Divided We Stand: The Crisis of a Frontierless Democracy.*

Webster, Daniel. *Works.*

Wendt, Lloyd and Kogan, Herman. *Big Bill of Chicago.*

Wertenbaker, Thomas Jefferson. *The Puritan Oligarchy: The Founding of American Civilization.*

Whipple, Leon. *Our Ancient Liberties: The Story of the Origin and Meaning of Civil and Religious Liberty in the United States.*

White, Theodore. *The Making of the President, 1964.*

William and Mary College. *Marshall, Wythe, Blackstone Commemoration Ceremonies, College of William and Mary, Saturday, September 25, 1954.*

Williams, T. Harry. *Huey Long.*

Wilson, Woodrow. *Cabinet Government in the United States.*

——. *A History of the American People.*

Wirt, William. *Sketches of the Life and Character of Patrick Henry.*

Wood, Harry. *Lew Davis: Twenty-Five Years of Painting in Arizona.*

Woodward, C. Vann. *Origins of the New South, 1877–1913.*

Woodward, W[illiam] E. *A New American History.*

Zunder, Theodore Albert. *The Early Days of Joel Barlow: A Connecticut Wit.*

American Law

Abernathy, Glenn. *The Right of Assembly and Association.*

American Bar Association. *The Prosecution Function and the Defense Function.*

Andrews, Israel Ward. *Manual of the Constitution of the United States.*

Antieau, Chester James; Downey, Arthur T.; Roberts, Edward C.; et al. *Freedom From Federal Establishment: Formation and Early History of the First Amendment Religion Clauses.*

Arnold, Thurman Wesley. *Fair Fights and Foul: A Dissenting Lawyer's Life.*

——. *Selections from the Letters and Legal Papers of Thurman Arnold.* 2 copies.

Baker, Liva. *Felix Frankfurter.*

Barth, Alan. *The Price of Liberty.*

Berman, Daniel M. *In Congress Assembled.*

Beth, Loren P. *Politics, the Constitution and the Supreme Court.*

Beveridge, Albert J. *The Life of John Marshall.*

Bickel, Alexander M. *The Least Dangerous Branch: The Supreme Court at the Bar of Politics.*

Biddle, Francis. *Justice Holmes, Natural Law and the Supreme Court.*

——. *Mr. Justice Holmes.*

Bigelow, John. *The Life of Samuel J. Tilden.*

Bingham, John Armor. *Trial of the Conspirators for the Assassination of President Lincoln and Company.*

Black, Charles L., Jr. *The Occasions of Justice.*

——. *The People and the Court.*

Black, Hugo L. (See Hugo L. Black).

Blanshard, Paul. *Religion and the Schools.*

Borkin, Joseph. *The Corrupt Judge: An Inquiry into Bribery and other High Crimes and Misdemeanors in Federal Courts.*

Brandeis, Louis Dembitz. *The Words of Justice Brandeis.*

Brannon, Henry. *A Treatise on the Rights and Privileges Guaranteed by the Fourteenth Amendment to the Constitution of the United States.*

Brant, Irving. *The Bill of Rights: Its Origin and Meaning.*

Brantley, William H. *Chief Justice Stone of Alabama.*

Brogan, D[enis] W[illiam]. *Politics and Law in the United States.*

Brooks, Aubrey Lee. *Walter Clark: Fighting Judge.*

Burton, Harold H. *The Occasional Papers of Mr. Justice Burton.*

Butler, Charles Henry. *A Century at the Bar of the Supreme Court of the United States.*

Cahn, Edmond. *Confronting Injustice: The Edmond Cahn Reader.*

——. *The Moral Decision.*

——. *The Sense of Injustice: An Anthropocentric View of the Law.*

——, ed. *The Great Rights.* 2 copies.

Cardozo, Benjamin N. *The Growth of the Law.*

——. *Law and Literature and Other Essays and Addresses.*

——. *The Nature of the Judicial Process.*

Chafee, Zechariah, Jr. *Free Speech in the United States.*

——. *Government and Mass Communications: A Report from the Commission on Freedom of the Press.*

——. *Three Human Rights in the Constitution of 1787.*

Chamberlain, Lawrence H. *Loyalty and Legislative Action: A Survey of Activity by the New York State Legislature 1919–1949.*

Clark, Charles E. *Procedure: The Handmaid of Justice.*

Clark, Floyd Barzilia. *The Constitutional Doctrines of Justice Harlan.*

Clark, Ramsey. *Crime in America.*

—— and Ervin, Sam J., Jr. *Role of the Supreme Court: Policymaker or Adjudicator.*

Clayton, James E. *The Making of Justice: The Supreme Court in Action.*

Cohen, Morris R. *Law and the Social Order: Essays in Legal Philosophy.*

Collins, Charles Wallace. *The Fourteenth Amendment and the States.*

Columbia Broadcasting System. *Oyez, Oyez, Oyez: Storm Over the Supreme Court.*

The Constitution of the United States of America, With the First Ten Amendments.

Corwin, Edward S. *Court Over Constitution.*

——. *Total War and the Constitution: Five Lectures Delivered on the William W. Cook Foundation at the University of Michigan, March 1946.*

——. *The Twilight of the Supreme Court.*

Coy, Harold. *The First Book of the Supreme Court.*

Craig, Alec. *Suppressed Books: A History of the Conception of Literary Obscenity* . . . .

Dilliard, Irving, ed. *Mr. Justice Brandeis, Great American.*

Drinan, Robert F. *Religion, the Courts and Public Policy.*

Douglas, William O. *An Almanac of Liberty.*

——. *A Living Bill of Rights.*

——. *The Right of the People.*

Edgerton, Henry W. *Freedom in the Balance: Opinions of Judge Henry W. Edgerton Relating to Civil Liberties.*

Emerson, Thomas I. and Haber, David. *Political and Civil Rights in the United States: A Collection of Legal and Related Materials.*

Ernst, Morris L. *The First Freedom.*

Fairman, Charles. *Mr. Justice Miller and the Supreme Court, 1862–1890.*

Findlay, Bruce Allyn and Esther Blair. *Your Rugged Constitution.*

Fortas, Abe. *Concerning Dissent and Civil Disobedience: We Have an Alternative to Violence.*

Frank, Jerome. *Courts on Trial: Myth and Reality in American Justice.* 2 copies.

——. *If Men Were Angels.*

Frank, John P. *Essays on Justice Hugo L. Black, Justice William O. Douglas, Justice Frank Murphy.*

——. *Justice Daniel Dissenting: A Biography of Peter V. Daniel, 1784–1860.*

——. *Lincoln as a Lawyer.* 2 copies.

——. *The Warren Court.*

Frankfurter, Felix. *The Commerce Clause Under Marshall, Taney and Waite.*

——. *Law and Politics: Occasional Papers of Felix Frankfurter, 1913–1938.*

——. *Mr. Justice Holmes and the Supreme Court.*

Freund, Paul A. *The Supreme Court of the United States.*

Friedman, Leon, ed. *Argument: The Oral Argument Before the Supreme Court in Brown v. Board of Education of Topeka, 1952–55.*

Friendly, Henry J. *In Praise of Erie and of the New Federal Common Law.*

Gellhorn, Walter. *Security, Loyalty, and Science.*

——, ed. *The States and Subversion.*

George, Beauford James, ed. *A New Look at Confessions: Escobedo, The Second Round.*

Gillette, William. *The Right to Vote: Politics and the Passage of the Fifteenth Amendment.*

Golden, Harry. *A Little Girl is Dead.*

Goldfarb, Ronald L. *The Contempt Power.*

——. *Ransom: A Critique of the American Bail System.*

Graham, Fred P. *The Self–Inflicted Wound.*

Griswold, Erwin N. *The Fifth Amendment.*

——. *Law and Lawyers in the United States: The Common Law Under Stress.*

Hawaii. *Constitution of the State of Hawaii, Agreed Upon by the Delegates of the People of Hawaii in Convention, at Iolani Palace . . . on July 22, 1950.*

Hellman, George S. *Benjamin N. Cardozo: American Judge.*

Holmes, Oliver W. *Justice Holmes to Doctor Wu: An Intimate Correspondence, 1921–1932.*

——, and Laski, Harold J. *Holmes-Laski Letters: The Correspondence of Mr. Justice Holmes and Harold J. Laski, 1916–35.*

——, and Pollock, Frederick. *Holmes-Pollock Letters: The Correspondence of Mr. Justice Holmes and Sir Frederick Pollock, 1874–1932.*

Howard, A. E. Dick. *The Road From Runnymede: Magna Carta and Constitutionalism in America.*

Howe, Mark DeWolfe. *Justice Oliver Wendell Holmes: The Shaping Years, 1841–1870.*

Huff, Martin. *The Rejection of Two Carolinians: Supreme Court Nominees Parker and Haynsworth . . . .*

Hughes, Frank. *Prejudice and the Press: A Restatement of the Principle of Freedom of the Press With Specific Reference to the Hutchins-Luce Commission.*

Hurst, James Willard. *The Growth of American Law: The Law Makers.*

——. *Justice Holmes on Legal History.*

Johns, Warren L. *Dateline Sunday, U.S.A.: The Story of Three and a Half Centuries of Sunday-Law Battles in America.*

Kalven, Harry, Jr. and Zeisel, Hans with Callahan, Thomas and Ennis, Philip. *The American Jury.*

Kaplan, Benjamin. *An Unhurried View of Copyright.*

Karlen, Delmar. *Judicial Administration: The American Experience.*

Kaufman, Irving L. *The Message, the Medium, and the First Amendment.*

Kintner, Earl W. *A Robinson-Patman Act Primer: A Businessman's Guide to the Law Against Price Discrimination . . . .*

Konefsky, Samuel J. *John Marshall and Alexander Hamilton: Architects of the American Constitution.*

——. *The Legacy of Holmes and Brandeis: A Study in the Influence of Ideas.*

Konvitz, Milton R. *Bill of Rights Reader: Leading Constitutional Cases.*

————. *A Century of Civil Rights, with a Study of State Law Against Discrimination by Theodore Leskes.*

————. *Fundamental Liberties of a Free People: Religion, Speech, Press, Assembly.* 2 copies.

Kragen, Adrian A. and McNulty, John K. *Cases and Materials on Federal Income Taxation.*

Laski, Harold J. *Studies in Law and Politics.*

Law Students of the University of Virginia, Under Grant from the Fund for the Republic, for the Committee on Civil Liberties and Civil Rights . . . of the American Bar Association. *Municipal Actions and Civil Liberties.*

Lehman, Irving. *Benjamin Nathan Cardozo: A Memorial.*

Lerner, Max, ed. *The Mind and Faith of Justice Holmes.*

Levy, Beryl Harold. *Cardozo and Frontiers of Legal Thinking, With Selected Opinions.*

Levy, Isaac D. and Smolens, Bernard J., comps. *Court Is In Session.*

Levy, Leonard W. *Legacy of Suppression: Freedom of Speech and Press in Early American History.*

Lewis, Anthony. *Gideon's Trumpet.*

Llewellyn, Karl N. *The Common Law Tradition: Deciding Appeals.*

Lockhart, William B.; Kamisar, Yale; and Choper, Jesse H. *Constitutional Law: Cases, Comments, Questions.*

MacIver, R[obert] M[orrison]. *The Ramparts We Guard.*

Mangels, Arthur C. and Byers, Albert L. *The Second Declaration of Independence.*

Mason, Alpheus Thomas. *Brandeis: A Free Man's Life.*

————. *Brandeis and the Modern State.*

————. *The Supreme Court: Palladium of Freedom.*

————. *William Howard Taft: Chief Justice.*

Mason, Lowell. *The Bull on the Bench.*

————. *The Language of Dissent.*

Mayers, Lewis. *Shall We Amend the Fifth Amendment?*

McCune, Wesley. *The Nine Young Men.*

Meador, Daniel John. *Preludes to Gideon.*

Mendelson, Wallace. *Justices Black and Frankfurter: Conflict in the Court.* 2 copies.

Miller, John C. *Crisis in Freedom: The Alien and Sedition Acts.* 2 copies.

Miller, Merle. *The Judges and the Judged.*

Morgan, Donald G. *Congress and the Constitution: A Study of Responsibility.*

Mott, Rodney L. *Due Process of Law.*

New York City Association of the Bar, Special Committee on the Study of Commitment Procedures and the Law Relating to Incompetents. *Mental Illness, Due Process, and the Criminal Defendant: A Second Report and Additional Recommendations* . . . .

New York, Supreme Court of the State of. *Exercises on the Occasion of the 250th Anniversary of its Founding: Albany, New York, May 28, 1941.*

Norris, Harold. *Mr. Justice Murphy and the Bill of Rights.*

Norton, Thomas James. *The Constitution of the United States: Its Sources and Its Application.* 2 copies.

Paschal, Joel Francis. *Mr. Justice Sutherland.*

Peare, Catherine Owens. *The Louis D. Brandeis Story.*

Pfeffer, Leo. *Church, State, and Freedom.*

——. *The Liberties of an American: The Supreme Court Speaks.*

Pound, Roscoe. *The Task of Law.*

Reel, A. Frank. *The Case of General Yamashita.*

Rembar, Charles. *The End of Obscenity: The Trials of Lady Chatterley, Tropic of Cancer and Fanny Hill.*

Rodell, Fred. *Nine Men: A Political History of the Supreme Court of the U.S. From 1790–1955.*

——. *Woe Unto You, Lawyers!*

Rogge, O. John. *The First and the Fifth, With Some Excursions Into Others.*

Rossiter, Clinton. *The Supreme Court and the Commander-in-Chief.*

Rostow, Eugene V. *The Sovereign Prerogative: The Supreme Court and the Quest for Law.*

Runes, Dagobert D. *The Disinherited and the Law.*

Rutledge, Wiley [Blount]. *A Declaration of Legal Faith.*

Sacco, Nicola and Vanzetti, Bartolomeo. *The Letters of Sacco and Vanzetti.*

Schroeder, Theodore. *A Challenge to Sex Censors.*

Schmulowitz, Nat. *The Laws of the Town of San Francisco, 1847.*

Schubert, Glendon A. *Constitutional Politics: The Political Behavior of Supreme Court Justices and the Constitutional Politics That They Make.*

Schuckers, J[acob] W. *The Life and Public Services of Salmon Portland Chase.*

Schwartz, Bernard. *A Commentary on the Constitution of the United States.*

Seagle, William. *The Quest for Law.*

Seldes, George. *Freedom of the Press.*

Seymour, Whitney North. *The Obligations of the Lawyer to His Profession.*

Sigler, Jay A. *Double Jeopardy: The Development of a Legal and Social Policy.*

Smith, James Barclay. *Studies in the Adequacy of the Constitution.*

Stryker, Lloyd Paul. *The Art of Advocacy: A Plea for the Renaissance of the Trial Lawyer.*

Sutherland, Arthur E. *Apology for Uncomfortable Change, 1865–1965.*

———, ed. *Government Under Law: Conference Held at Harvard Law School on the Occasion of the Bicentennial of John Marshall, Chief Justice of the United States, 1801–1835.*

Swisher, Carl Brent. *American Constitutional Development.*

———. *The Growth of Constitutional Power in the United States.*

———. *Stephen J. Field.*

Taylor, Hannis. *Due Process of Law and Equal Protection.*

Todd, A[lden] L. *Justice on Trial: The Case of Louis D. Brandeis.*

Traynor, Roger J. *The Devils of Due Process in Criminal Detection, Detention, and Trial.*

U.S. Commission on Civil Rights. *Report.*

U.S. Congress. *Debates on the Judiciary . . . During the First Session of the Seventh Congress. . . .*

U.S. Congress: House of Representatives. *Proceedings at the Ceremonies in Commemoration of the 150th Anniversary of the First Meeting of the Supreme Court of the United States.*

U.S. Constitution Sesquicentennial Commission. *The Story of the Constitution 1787–1937.*

U.S. National Commission on Reform of Federal Criminal Laws. *Working Papers . . . .*

U.S. President's Water Policy Commission. . . . *Water Resources Law: The Report of the President.*

Virginia Commission on Constitutional Government, comp. *We The States: An Anthology of Historic Documents and Commentaries Thereon, Expounding the State and Federal Relationships.*

Warren, Charles. *The Supreme Court in United States History.*

Warren, Earl. *Address Delivered at the 46th Annual Meeting of the American Law Institute, May 20, 1969.*

———. *Hughes and the Court.*

———. *The Public Papers of Chief Justice Earl Warren.*

Westin, Alan F. *The Anatomy of a Constitutional Law Case: Youngstown Sheet and Tube Co. v. Sawyer, the Steel Seizure Decision.*

———, ed. *An Autobiography of the Supreme Court: Speeches, Letters, Memoirs of Justices, 1790–1961.*

Whipple, Leon. *Our Ancient Liberties: The Story of the Origin and Meaning of Civil and Religious Liberty in the United States.*

Wyzanski, Charles E., Jr. *Whereas, A Judge's Premises: Essays in Judgment, Ethics, and the Law.*

Hugo L. Black

Berman, Daniel M. *The Measure Is Man: The Political Philosophy of Hugo L. Black.*

Black, Hugo LaFayette. *A Constitutional Faith.*

———. *Crença na Constituição.* 2 copies.

Dilliard, Irving. *One Man's Stand for Freedom: Mr. Justice Black and the Bill of Rights.*

Frank, John P. *Essays on Justice Hugo L. Black, Justice William O. Douglas, Justice Frank Murphy.*

———. *Mr. Justice Black, the Man and His Opinions.*

Mason, Gene L. *Hugo Black and the United States Senate.* 2 copies.

Mendelson, Wallace. *Justices Black and Frankfurter: Conflict in the Court.* 2 copies.

Shmalo, Nathan S. *An Inquiry into the Voting Behavior of Justice Black During the 1960's: A Qualitative Attempt to Explain a Bloc Phenomenon.*

Strickland, Stephen Parks, ed. *Hugo Black and the Supreme Court.*

Williams, Charlotte. *Hugo Black.* 2 copies.

Contemporary Affairs

American Civil Liberties Union. *Secret Detention by the Chicago Police.*

———. *Work Ahead in Hope: 39th Annual Report July 1, 1958 to June 30, 1959.*

Barrett, Edward L., Jr. *The Tenney Committee: Legislative Investigation of Subversive Activities in California.*

Barth, Alan. *Government by Investigation.*

Berelson, Bernard and Janowitz, Morris, eds. *Reader in Public Opinion and Communication.*

Birmingham, Stephen. *The Right People: A Portrait of the American Social Establishment.*

Blanshard, Paul. *God and Man in Washington.*

Bontecou, Eleanor. *The Federal Loyalty-Security Program.*

Browder, Earl. *Victory and After.*

Cahn, Edgar S., ed. *Our Brother's Keeper: The Indian in White America.*

Carr, Robert K. *The House Committee on Un-American Activities 1945–1950.*

Carter, Richard. *Breakthrough: The Saga of Jonas Salk.*

Chafee, Zechariah, Jr. *Government and Mass Communications: A Report from the Commission on Freedom of the Press.*

Clark, Ramsey. *Crime in America.*

Commager, Henry Steele. *Freedom, Loyalty, Dissent.*

———. *Freedom and Order.*

Countryman, Vern. *Un-American Activities in the State of Washington: The Work of the Canwell Committee.*

Davies, Arthur Powell. *The Urge to Persecute.*

Du Puy, William Atherton. *Hawaii and Its Race Problem.*

Ernst, Morris L. and Schwartz, Alan U. *Censorship: The Search for the Obscene.*

Gellhorn, Walter. *Security, Loyalty, and Science.*

Golden, Harry. *Only in America.*

Graf, William, comp. *Platforms of the Two Great Political Parties: 1932 to 1944.*

Grimes, Alan P. *Equality in America: Religion, Race, and the Urban Majority.*

Hackett, Francis. *What Mein Kampf Means to America.*

Hamilton, Walton. *The Politics of Industry.*

Harris, Robert Jennings. *The Quest for Equality: The Constitution, Congress, and the Supreme Court.*

Hewlett, Richard and Duncan, Francis. *Atomic Shield, 1947–1952.*

Hoffer, Eric. *The Ordeal of Change.*

Hofstadter, Richard. *The American Political Tradition.*

———. *Anti-Intellectualism in American Life.*

Howard, A. E. Dick. *Journeys Through Foreign Lands.*

Inglis, Ruth A. *Freedom of the Movies: A Report on Self-Regulation From the Commission on Freedom of the Press.*

Kallen, Horace M. *What I Believe and Why—Maybe: Essays for the Modern World.*

Kennedy, John F. *Dedication; The Gift Outright; The Inaugural Address: Washington, D.C., January the twentieth, 1961.*

Kennedy, Joseph P. *I'm For Roosevelt.*

Laski, Harold J. *The American Presidency: An Interpretation.*

———. *The Danger of Being a Gentleman, and Other Essays.*

———. *Faith, Reason, and Civilization: An Essay in Historical Analysis.*

———. *The Labour Party, The War and the Future.*

———. *Reflections on the Revolution of Our Time.*

———. *The Strategy of Freedom: An Open Letter to American Youth.*

———. *Studies in Law and Politics.*

——. *Where Do We Go From Here?*

——. *Will Planning Restrict Freedom?*

Lazarsfeld, Paul F.; Berelson, Bernard; and Gaudet, Hazel. *The People's Choice: How the Voter Makes Up His Mind in a Presidential Campaign.*

Lerner, Max. *Actions and Passions: Notes on the Multiple Revolution of Our Time.*

——. *America as a Civilization: Life and Thought in the United States Today.*

——. *Ideas For the Ice Age: Studies in a Revolutionary Era.*

Lewis, Anthony and the New York Times. *Portrait of a Decade: The Second American Revolution: Civil Rights Struggle From 1954–64.*

Lippman, Walter. *An Inquiry Into the Principles of the Good Society.*

Madison, Charles A. *Leaders and Liberals in 20th Century America.*

Mann, Thomas. *This Peace: Together With the Address of November 9, 1938.*

Manning, Joseph Columbus. *Fadeout of Populism: Presenting, in Connection, the Political Combat Between the Pot and the Kettle.*

Newman, James R. *The Rule of Folly.*

Norris, George W. *Peace Without Hate: A Lecture Delivered at the University of Nebraska.*

Oates, James F., Jr. *Business and Social Change: Life Insurance Looks to the Future.*

Ogden, August Raymond. *The Dies Committee: A Study of the Special House Committee for the Investigation of Un-American Activities, 1938–1944.*

Parrington, Vernon Louis. *Main Currents in American Thought.*

Pater, Alan F. and Landau, Milton, comps. and arrangers. *What They Said in 1937: The Yearbook of Oral Opinion.*

Pearson, Drew and Anderson, Jack. *The Case Against Congress: A Compelling Indictment of Corruption on Capitol Hill.*

Quigley, Carroll. *Tragedy and Hope: A History of the World in Our Time.*

Reich, Charles A. *The Greening of America.*

Reston, James. *Sketches in the Sand.*

Roosevelt, Frankln Delano and Pius XII. *Wartime Correspondence Between President Roosevelt and Pope Pius XII.*

Ross, Malcolm. *All Manner of Men: The Racial Crisis in American Life.*

Ryan, John A. *Questions of the Day.*

Sandburg, Carl. *An Address Before a Joint Session of Congress, February 12, 1959.*

Schlesinger, Arthur M., Jr. *The Politics of Hope.*

——. *The Vital Center.*

Seldes, George. *The Facts Are . . . A Guide to Falsehood and Propaganda in the Press and Radio.*

Shalit, Gene and Grossman, Lawrence K. *Somehow It Works: A Candid Portrait of the 1964 Presidential Election by NBC News.*

Stewart, George R. *The Year of the Oath: The Fight for Academic Freedom at the University of California.*

Taylor, Telford. *Nuremberg and Vietnam: An American Tragedy.*

Thomas, Elbert D. *The Four Fears.*

Truman, Harry S. *Mr. Citizen.*

Underwood, Oscar W. *Drifting Sands of Party Politics.*

U.S. Commission on Civil Rights. *Report.*

U.S. Congress: Senate Committee on Foreign Relations. *State Department Employee Loyalty Investigation and Part 2, Individual Views of Senator Lodge.*

U.S. Congress: Senate Committee on Foreign Relations. *State Department Employee Loyalty Investigation: Hearings Before a Subcommittee.*

U.S. Congress: Special Senate Committee on Investigation of Air Mail and Ocean Mail Contracts. *Hearings.*

U.S. National Advisory Commission on Civil Disorders. *Supplemental Studies.*

Warren, Earl. *Address Delivered at the 46th Annual Meeting of the American Law Institute, May 20, 1969.*

Wells, H[erbert] G[eorge]. *The Rights of Man, or, What Are We Fighting For?*

Westin, Alan F. *Privacy and Freedom.*

Weyl, Nathaniel. *The Battle Against Disloyalty.*

Whitehead, Alfred North. *The Aims of Education.*

English History, Biography, and Law

Aiken, William Appleton and Henning, Basil D., eds. *Conflict in Stuart England: Essays in Honour of Wallace Notestein.*

Baker, Timothy. *The Normans: The Men Who Made the English-Speaking World.*

Bentham, Jeremy. *A Fragment on Government.*

——. *Principles of Morals and Legislation.*

——. *Theory of Legislation.*

Bowen, Catherine Drinker. *The Lion and the Throne: The Life and Times of Sir Edward Coke (1552–1634).*

Buckle, Henry Thomas. *History of Civilization in England.*

Campbell, Lord. *Lives of the Lord Chancellors and Keepers of the Great Seal of England.*

Carlyle, Thomas. *Critical and Miscellaneous Essays.*

——. *Oliver Cromwell's Letters and Speeches.*

Carpenter, Edward. *England's Ideal and Other Papers on Social Subjects.*

Churchill, Winston S. *The Grand Alliance: The Second World War.*

Elizabeth II. *The Form and Order of the Service That Is To Be Performed and the Ceremonies That Are To Be Observed in the Coronation of Her Majesty Queen Elizabeth II in the Abbey Church of St. Peter, Westminster, on Tuesday the Second Day of June 1953.*

Erskine, Thomas. *Speeches of Lord Erskine, While at the Bar.*

Evershed, Francis Raymond. *The Practical and Academic Characteristics of English Law.*

Fox, Charles James. *The Speeches of the Right Honourable Charles James Fox, in the House of Commons.*

Frank, Joseph. *The Levellers: A History of the Writings of Three Seventeenth-Century Social Democrats, John Lilburne, Richard Overton, William Walwyn.*

Fraser, Antonia. *Mary, Queen of Scots.*

Guizot, François Pierre Guillaume. *History of England From the Earliest Times.*

Gunsaulus, Frank Wakeley. *William Ewart Gladstone.*

Hallam, Henry. *The Constitutional History of England: From the Accession of Henry VII to the Death of George II.*

Hawarde, John. *Les Reportes Del Cases in Camera Stellata, 1593 to 1609.*

Hibbert, Christopher. *Charles I.*

Hoggart, Richard. *The Uses of Literacy: Changing Patterns in English Mass Culture.*

Hollander, Barnett. *The English Bar, A Priesthood: The Tribute of An American Lawyer.*

Laski, Harold J. *Parliamentary Government in England: A Commentary.*

Macaulay, Thomas Babington. *Critical and Historical Essays.*

——. *The History of England From the Accession of James II.*

Mackintosh, James. *Memoirs of the Life of the Right Honorable Sir James Mackintosh.*

Martin, Kingsley. *Harold Laski (1893–1950): A Biographical Memoir.*

Ogg, Frederic Austin. *English Government and Politics.*

Orations of British Orators.

Robertson, J[ohn] M[ackinnon]. *The Evolution of States: An Introduction to English Politics.*

Spencer, Hazelton. *The Art and Life of William Shakespeare.*

Stanley, Arthur Penrhyn. *Historical Memorials of Westminster Abbey.*

Stryker, Lloyd Paul. *For the Defense: Thomas Erskine, the Most Enlightened Liberal of His Times, 1750–1823.*

Trevelyan, G[eorge] M[acaulay]. *The Tudors and the Stuart Era.*

Trevelyan, George Otto. *The Early History of Charles James Fox.*

Wells, H[erbert] G[eorge]. *The Rights of Man, or, What Are We Fighting For?*

ENGLISH LITERATURE

Addison, Joseph. *The Spectator.*

Bunyan, John. *The Complete Works of John Bunyan.*

Cronin, A[rchibald] J[oseph]. *The Stars Look Down.*

Dickens, Charles. *The Posthumous Papers of the Pickwick Club.*

Miller, George Morey, ed. *English Literature: The Victorian Period.*

Milton, John. *Areopagitica and Other Prose Works.*

——. *The Prose Works of John Milton, With a Life of the Author* . . . .

Reed, Albert Granberry, ed. *English Literature: The Romantic Period.*

Shakespeare, William. *The Complete Works of William Shakespeare.* 2 editions.

——. *Hamlet: A Television Script.*

——. *The Plays and Poems of Shakespeare.*

Shakespeare's Works.

Shaw, Bernard. *Nine Plays with Prefaces and Notes.*

Spencer, Hazelton. *The Art and Life of William Shakespeare.*

Tagore, Rabindranath. *The Gardener.*

EUROPEAN HISTORY, BIOGRAPHY, AND LAW

Bowers, Claude G. *Pierre Vergniaud: Voice of the French Revolution.*

Carlyle, Thomas. *Frederick the Great.*

Draper, John William. *History of the Intellectual Development of Europe.*

Guizot, François Pierre Guillaume. *The History of Civilization in Europe.*

Hallam, Henry. *History of Europe During the Middle Ages.*

——. *View of the State of Europe During the Middle Ages.*

Hitler, Adolf. *Mein Kampf.*

Korwin-Rhodes, Marta. *The Mask of Warriors: The Siege of Warsaw, September 1939.*

de La Fuye, Maurice, and Babeau, Emile. *The Apostle of Liberty: A Life of Lafayette.*

The Life and History of Lewis XIV, Present King of France and Navarre.

Macaulay, Thomas Babington. *Critical and Historical Essays.*

Maurois, André. *Adrienne: The Life of the Marquise de LaFayette.*

Munro, William Bennett. *The Governments of Europe.*

Pares, Bernard. *Russia: Its Past and Present.*

Prescott, William H. *History of the Reign of Ferdinand and Isabella, the Catholic.*

Rothfels, Hans. *The German Opposition to Hitler.*

Veblen, Thorstein. *Imperial Germany and the Industrial Revolution.*

Watson, Thomas E. *Napoleon: A Sketch of His Life, Character, Struggles and Achievements.*

———. *The Story of France, From the Earliest Times to the Consulate of Napoleon Bonaparte.*

Watson, Thomas J. *Unconquerable: A Review of the Historic Visit to the United States and Canada Which Was Made During June and July, 1942, by His Majesty Peter II, King of Yugoslavia.*

Whitlock, Brand. *La Fayette.*

FICTION

[Abbott, Jacob]. *Jonas, A Judge, or, Law Among the Boys.*

Asch, Sholem. *The Nazarene.*

Brannon, Peter A. *A Little Black Volume: The Story of Curiosity's Reward.*

Douglas, Lloyd C. *The Robe.*

Dozier, Orion T. *Poems and Prose.*

Fast, Howard. *The American.* 2 copies.

———. *The Passion of Sacco and Vanzetti: A New England Legend.*

———. *Spartacus.*

Hersey, John. *The Wall.*

Huxley, Aldous. *Brave New World Revisited.*

Joyce, James. *Ulysses.*

Kimbrough, Edward. *Night Fire.*

Kipling, Rudyard. *Mulvaney Stories.*

More Heart Throbs.

Radin, Max. *The Day of Reckoning.*

Tolstoy, Leo. *War and Peace.*

Touhy, Roger with Brennan, Ray. *The Stolen Years.*

[Vining], Elizabeth Janet Gray. *Anthology With Comments.*

GREECE

Aeschylus. *Aeschylus' Prometheus Bound and the Seven Against Thebes.*

Aesop. *Aesop's Fables.*

Aristophanes. *The Comedies of Aristophanes.*

Aristotle. *Aristotle's Constitution of Athens and Related Texts.*

——. *Aristotle's History of Animals, in Ten Books.*

——. *Metaphysics, Books X–XIV, with English Translation by Hugh Tredennick, and Oeconomica and Magna Moralia, With English Translation by G. Cyril Armstrong.*

——. *Aristotle's Politics: A Treatise on Government.*

——. *Aristotle's Treatise on Rhetoric, Literally Translated from the Greek, With an Analysis by Thomas Hobbes, and a Series of Questions. Also, the Poetic of Aristotle, Literally Translated . . . by Theodore Buckley.*

Barr, Stringfellow. *The Will of Zeus: A History of Greece From the Origins of Hellenic Culture to the Death of Alexander.*

Benson, E[dward] F[rederic]. *The Life of Alcibiades, The Idol of Athens.*

Bonner, Robert J. *Lawyers and Litigants in Ancient Athens: The Genesis of the Legal Profession.*

—— and Smith, Gertrude. *The Administration of Justice from Homer to Aristotle.*

Bury, John Bagnell. *A History of Greece to the Death of Alexander the Great.*

Chamoux, François. *The Civilization of Greece.*

Diogenes, Laertius. *Lives of Eminent Philosophers.*

Durant, Will. *The Life of Greece.*

Euripides. *Five Plays of Euripides: Alcestis, Media, The Trojan Women, Iphigenia in Tauris, Electra.*

——. *The Hippolytus of Euripides.*

Fairbanks, Arthur. *Greek Gods and Heroes, As Represented in the Classical Collection of the Museum: A Handbook for High School Students Prepared in Conjunction with a Committee of Teachers.*

Grote, George. *Plato, and the Other Companions of Sokrates.*

Hamilton, Edith. *The Echo of Greece.*

——. *The Greek Way.*

——. *Mythology*.

Hamilton, Elizabeth. *Memoirs of the Life of Agrippina, the Wife of Germanicus*.

Herodotus. *The History of Herodotus of Halicarnassus*.

Homer. *The Iliad*.

Isocrates.

Jaeger, Werner. *Paideia: The Ideals of Greek Culture*.

Lucian. *A True History*.

Mahaffy, John Pentland. *History of Greece and of the Greek People*.

Parsons, Edward Alexander. *The Alexandrian Library: Glory of the Hellenic World*.

Plato. *Apology, Crito, Republic I–II*.

——. *Dialogues of Plato*. 2 copies.

——. *Plato's The Republic*.

Plutarch. *Plutarch's Lives: The Lives of the Noble Grecians and Romans*. 2 editions.

——. *Plutarch's Writings: Essays and Miscellaneous*.

Polwhele, Richard, tr. *The Idyllia, Epigrams, and Fragments, of Theocritus, Bion, and Moschus, With the Elegies of Tyrtaeus*.

Potter, John. *Archaeologica Graeca, or, the Antiquities of Greece*.

Procopius. *Secret History of Procopius*.

Robinson, Charles A., Jr., ed. *An Anthology of Greek Drama*.

de Sélincourt, Aubrey. *The World of Herodotus*.

Taylor, A[lfred] E[dward]. *Socrates: The Man and His Thoughts*.

Thucydides. *The Peloponnesian War*.

Thucydides Translated into English.

Toynbee, Arnold J. *Greek Civilization and Character*. 2 copies.

Warner, Rex. *Pericles the Athenian*.

Zimmern, Alfred. *The Greek Commonwealth: Politics and Economics in Fifth Century Athens*.

Thomas Jefferson

Adams, James Truslow. *The Living Jefferson*.

Boorstin, Daniel J. *The Lost World of Thomas Jefferson*.

Bowers, Claude G. *Jefferson and Hamilton: The Struggle for Democracy in America*.

——. *Jefferson in Power: The Death Struggle of the Federalists*.

[Carpenter, Stephen C.]. *Memoirs of the Honorable Thomas Jefferson . . . , Containing a Concise History of Those States, From the Acknowledgement of Their Independence With a View of the Rise and Progress of French Influence and French Principles in That Country.*

Foley, John P., ed. *The Jeffersonian Cyclopedia.*

Jefferson, Thomas. *Democracy.*

——. *The Life and Morals of Jesus of Nazareth.*

——. *A Manual of Parliamentary Practice . . . the Whole Brought Down to the Practice of the Present Time; To Which are Added the Rules and Orders, Together With the Joint Rules of Both Houses of Congress . . . .*

——. *Memoir, Correspondence, and Miscellanies, From the Papers of Thomas Jefferson.*

——. *The Papers of Thomas Jefferson.*

Koch, Adrienne. *Jefferson and Madison: The Great Collaboration.*

Malone, Dumas. *Jefferson and the Rights of Man.*

——. *Jefferson the Virginian.*

Padover, Saul K., ed. *Thomas Jefferson and the National Capital, 1783–1818.*

Tyler, John, and 18 others. *A Selection of Eulogies in Honor of Those Illustrious Patriots and Statesmen, John Adams and Thomas Jefferson.*

Watson, Thomas E. *The Life and Times of Thomas Jefferson.*

Miscellaneous

Amadeo, Santos P. *Argentine Constitutional Law: The Judicial Function in the Maintenance of the Federal System and the Preservation of Individual Rights.*

Arcaya, Pedro Manuel. *The Gomez Regime in Venezuela and Its Background.*

Argosy Book Store. *Catalogue 505: Americana, From the Collection of Andrew Christian Zabriskie and Ilo Orleans, With Other Recent Acquisitions.*

Art Students' League of New York. *73rd Regular Session: September 15, 1948 to May 27, 1949.*

Art and Understanding.

Aspen Institute for Humanistic Studies. *Aspen Executives' Program: First and Second Weeks' Readings.*

Bellamy, Edward. *Looking Backward 2000–1887.*

Bingham, Lois A. *How to Look at Works of Art: The Search for Line.*

Block, Herbert. *The Herblock Gallery.*

Bone, Robert G. *Ancient History With Questions and Answers.*

Brewer, David J., ed. *World's Best Orations.* 2 copies.

Bulfinch, Thomas. *The Age of Fable or Beauties of Mythology.*

——. *Bulfinch's Mythology: The Age of Fable, The Age of Chivalry, Legends of Charlemagne.*

Byars, William Vincent, ed. *The Handbook of Oratory.*

Cairns, Huntington; Tate, Allen; and Van Doren, Mark, eds. *Invitation to Learning.*

Childs, Marquis W. *Sweden: The Middle Way.*

Clark, Sydney. *All the Best in Japan, with Manila, Hong Kong and Macao.*

Clarke, Joseph I. C. *Robert Emmet: A Tragedy of Irish History.*

Cohen, Benjamin V. *The United Nations: Constitutional Developments, Growth and Possibilities.*

Cooke, Alistair. *A Commencement Address.*

Curtis, Charles P., Jr. and Greenslet, Ferris, eds. *The Practical Cogitator.*

Dwight, Timothy, et al, eds. *The World's Great Classics.*

Eliot, Charles W., ed. *Harvard Classics.*

Fattorusso, Giuseppe and M. L., eds. *Wonders of Italy.*

Free Speech Library. *Book List.*

Galloway, Thomas Walton. *The Father and His Boy: The Place of Sex in Manhood Making.*

Gilder, Jeannette L., ed. *Masterpieces of the World's Best Literature.*

Goldberg, Dorothy. *The Creative Woman.*

Golden, Frances Leo. *Laughter is Legal.*

Golden, Harry. *The Israelis: Portrait of a People.*

Grant, M[elville] R[osyn]. *True Principles of Freemasonry.*

Gray, Randal Lockhart, comp. *Wit, Wisdom and Eloquence.*

Grigson, Geoffrey and Gibbs-Smith, Charles Harvard, eds. *Things. People. Ideas. Places.*

Hallam, Henry. *Literature of Europe.*

Harris, Sydney J. *On the Contrary.*

Hauser, Gayelord. *Look Younger, Live Longer.*

Hayes, Helen and Funke, Lewis. *A Gift of Joy.*

Hermann, Paul. *Conquest by Man.*

History of Freemasonry and Concordant Orders.

Hodgkins, Henry Bell. *Quotes and Rhymes From Other Times.*

Holmes, George Sanford. *"Yes, This Is Washington!": Shrines and Sonnets of the Potomac Shore.*

India, Supreme Court of. *Opinion of the Supreme Court of India on Special Reference No. 1 of 1964. (Reference by the President of India under Art. 143(1) of the Constitution of India Regarding the Powers and Jurisdiction of the High Court and Its Judges.)*

Ives, Burl. *The Burl Ives Songbook.*

Johnson, Rossiter, ed. *Masterpieces of Eloquence: A Library of Ancient and Modern Oratory, with Critical Studies of the World's Greatest Orators.*

Jones, Howard Mumford. *One Great Society: Humane Learning in the U.S.*

Karpin, Fred L. *The Point-Count System of Bidding in Contract Bridge.*

Kennedy, John F. and Others. *Creative America: Collection of Photos and Short Articles.*

Klee, Paul. *Paintings, Drawings, and Prints by Paul Klee.*

Koestler, Arthur. *Reflections on Hanging.*

Kogan, Herman. *The Great EB: The Story of the Encyclopaedia Britannica.*

Kraft, James Lewis. *Adventure in Jade.*

Lavin, John. *A Halo for Gomez.*

Lee, Irving J. *Language Habits in Human Affairs: An Introduction to General Semantics.*

Liebetrau, Preben. *Oriental Rugs in Colour.*

Lowie, Robert H. *Primitive Society.*

Margolin, Robert, comp. *The Little Pun Book.*

Morals and Dogma of the Ancient and Accepted Scottish Rite of Freemasonry.

Morgan, Joy Elmer, ed. *The American Citizens Handbook.*

Muller, Leon Arnold. *Spirit of Youth: Universal Secular Art.*

National Geographic Magazine. *Everyday Life in Ancient Times: Highlights of the Beginnings of Western Civilization in Mesopotamia, Egypt, Greece, and Rome.*

Nehru, B[raj] K[umar]. *Speaking of India.*

O'Connor, Basil. *Man's Responsibility in the Fight Against Disease.*

Peterson, Houston, ed. *A Treasury of the World's Great Speeches.*

[Pinkerton, John]. *The Treasury of Wit.*

Proxmire, Ellen. *One Foot in Washington: The Perilous Life of a Senator's Wife.*

Ramaswamy, M. *Some Suggestions for the Modification of the Draft Constitution of India.*

Rodell, Fred. *Her Infinite Variety: Portraits of Thirty-Six Women Around The World.*

Rollin, Charles. *The Ancient History of the Egyptians, Carthaginians, Assyrians, Babylonians, Medes and Persians, Macedonians and Grecians.*

Romm, Alexander. *Matisse: A Social Critique.*

Rosenkranz, Joseph Aaron. *Sixty Stray Thoughts Jotted Down Along the Avenue of Life.*

Sanderson, Edgar; Lamberton, John Porter; Morris, Charles; and Others. *Literature of the 19th Century.*

Scott, Winifred. *Is Your Death Inevitable?*

Seldes, Gilbert. *The Great Audience.*

Shawn, Ted. *Whitman: His Immortal Leaves.*

Sherwood, Mrs. John. *Manners and Social Usages.*

Smith, Darrel Hevenor. . . . *The Forest Service: Its History, Activities, and Organization* . . . .

Squire, Anne. *Social Washington.*

Strode, Hudson. *Finland Forever.*

———. *The Story of Bermuda.*

———. *Timeless Mexico.*

Strunk, William, Jr. and White, E. B. *The Elements of Style.*

Thorndike, Ashley H., ed. *Modern Eloquence.*

Van Loon, Hendrik Willem. *Van Loon's Lives.*

Wilson, Epiphanius, ed. *Oriental Literature.*

Wollstonecraft, Mary. *The Rights of Woman.*

Philosophy, Jurisprudence, and Religion

Acton, First Baron [John Emerich Edward Dahlberg-Acton]. *Essays on Freedom and Power.*

Arnold, Thurman Wesley. *The Folklore of Capitalism.*

———. *The Symbols of Government.*

Bacon, Francis. *Advancement of Learning and Novum Organum.*

———. *The Works of Francis Bacon, . . . and Lord High Chancellor of England.*

Barrett, William. *What Is Existentialism?*

Bentham, Jeremy. *A Fragment on Government.*

———. *An Introduction to the Principles of Morals and Legislation.*

———. *Theory of Legislation.*

Bergson, Henri. *An Introduction to Metaphysics.*

Bernstein, Philip S. *What the Jews Believe.*

The Holy Bible.

The New English Bible: New Testament.

The New Indexed Bible.

Blanshard, Paul. *American Freedom and Catholic Power.*

Brecht, Arnold. *The Political Philosophy of Arnold Brecht.*

Bury, John Bagnell. *A History of Freedom of Thought.*

Butts, R. Freeman. *The American Tradition in Religion and Education.*

Cahn, Edmond. *Confronting Injustice: The Edmond Cahn Reader.*

——. *The Moral Decision.*

——. *The Predicament of Democratic Man.*

Cairns, Huntington. *Law and Its Premises.*

Calamandrei, Piero. *Eulogy of Judges.*

Camus, Albert. *Resistance, Rebellion, and Death.*

Carrell, Alexis. *Man, The Unknown.*

Chandler, Walter M. *The Trial of Jesus: From a Lawyer's Standpoint.*

Chipman, Nathaniel. *Principles of Government: A Treatise on Free Institutions Including the Constitution of the United States.*

Cohen, Morris R. *The Faith of a Liberal: Selected Essays.*

——. *Law and the Social Order: Essays in Legal Philosophy.*

——. *A Preface to Logic.*

Confucius. *The Wisdom of Confucius.*

Cranston, Maurice. *What Are Human Rights?*

D'Argenson, Marquis [Renë Louis de Voyer de Paulmy]. *Essays: Civil, Moral, Literary and Political.*

Davies, Arthur Powell. *The Faith of an Unrepentant Liberal.*

——. *The Ten Commandments.*

Dawson, Miles Menander, arranger. *The Conduct of Life: The Ethics of Confucius.*

Dewey, John. *Logic: The Theory of Inquiry.*

——. *The Quest for Certainty: A Study of the Relation of Knowledge and Action.*

DiSalle, Michael Vincent with Blochman, Lawrence G. *The Power of Life or Death.*

Draper, John William. *History of the Conflict Between Religion and Science.*

Eliopoulos, Nicholas C. *Oneness of Politics and Religion.*

Famous Utopias: Being the Complete Text of Rousseau's Social Contract, More's Utopia, Bacon's New Atlantis, Campanella's City of the Sun.

Frank, Jerome. *Law and the Modern Mind.*

Frazer, James G. *The Golden Bough: A Study in Magic and Religion.*

Gaer, Joseph. *The Wisdom of the Living Religions.*

Garrison, William Lloyd. *On Non-Resistance.*

Gibran, Kahlil. *The Prophet.*

Gwaltney, Leslie Lee. *The World's Greatest Decade: The Times and the Baptists.*

Halsey, Margaret. *The Pseudo-Ethic: A Speculation on American Politics and Morals.*

Hobbes, Thomas. *Leviathan: Or the Matter, Forme and Power of a Commonwealth, Ecclesiastical and Civil.*

Howlett, Duncan. *The Fourth American Faith.*

Huegli, Albert G., ed. *Church and State Under God.*

Jones, Howard Mumford, ed. *Primer of Intellectual Freedom.*

Kallen, Horace M. *The Education of Free Men: An Essay Toward a Philosophy of Education.*

——. *Liberty, Laughter and Tears: Reflections on the Relations of Comedy and Tragedy to Human Freedom.*

Komroff, Manuel, ed. *The Authorized Version of the Apocrypha.*

Konvitz, Milton R. *Fundamental Liberties of a Free People: Religion, Speech, Press, Assembly.*

Krishnamurti, Jiddu. *Authentic Notes of Discussions and Talks Given by Krishnamurti.*

——. *The Kingdom of Happiness.*

Lamsa, George M. *The New Testament According to Eastern Text.*

Lerner, Max. *Ideas Are Weapons.*

Link, Henry C. *The Rediscovery of Morals.*

Littell, Franklin Hamlin. *From State Church to Pluralism: A Protestant Interpretation of Religion in American History.*

Locke, John. *Essay Concerning Human Understanding.*

——. *Treatise of Civil Government and a Letter Concerning Toleration.*

MacIver, R[obert] M[orrison], ed. *Great Expressions of Human Rights: A Series of Addresses and Discussions.*

Maine, Henry Sumner. *Ancient Law.*

Mannheim, Karl. *Freedom, Power and Democratic Planning.*

Mason, Alpheus Thomas. *Free Government in the Making: Readings in American Political Thought.*

Marx, Karl. *Capital: A Critical Analysis of Capitalist Production.*

Mazzuchelli, [Samuel Charles]. *Memoirs: Historical and Edifying of a Missionary Apostolic of the Order of Saint Dominic Among Various Indian Tribes and Among the Catholics and Protestants in the United States of America.*

Meiklejohn, Alexander. *Free Speech and Its Relation to Self-Government.*

Mill, John Stuart. *Principles of Political Economy.*

——. *Three Essays: On Liberty; Representative Government; The Subjection of Women.*

de Montesquieu, Baron (Charles de Secondat). *The Spirit of Laws, Including D'Alembert's Analysis of the Work.*

Muller, Herbert Joseph. *The Uses of the Past: Profiles of Former Societies.*

Noonan, John T., ed. *The Morality of Abortion: Legal and Historical Perspectives.*

Northrop, F[ilmer] S[tuart] C[uckow]. *The Complexity of Legal and Ethical Experience: Studies in the Method of Normative Subjects.*

Norton, Charles Ledyard. *Political Americanism.*

Nowell-Smith, Patrick Horace. *Ethics.*

Oriental Treasures: Wisdom From the Great Inspirational Books of Asia.

Pope John XXIII. *Mater et Magistra: An Encyclical Letter of His Holiness.*

Russell, Bertrand. *Education and the Good Life.*

——. *Political Ideals.*

Sample, Robert Fleming. *Beacon-Lights of the Reformation, or, Romanism and the Reformers.*

The Secret of the Golden Flower: A Chinese Book of Life.

Selsam, Howard. *What is Philosophy? A Marxist Introduction.*

Smith, Arthur Delafield. *The Right to Life.*

Smith, John E., ed. *Contemporary American Philosophy.*

Smith, Joseph Jr., tr. *The Book of Mormon.*

Spinoza, Benedictus de. *Improvement of the Understanding, Ethics, and Correspondence.*

Stourzh, Gerald, and Lerner, Ralph, eds. *Readings in American Democracy.*

Syracuse University: Maxwell Graduate School of Citizenship and Public Affairs. *The Three Syracuses and the Three-P Professorship: Being Syntheses of Poetry, Politics, and Philosophy as Disclosed on T.V. Smith Day, Syracuse University, November 10, 1948.*

Teilhard de Chardin, Pierre. *The Phonomenon of Man.*

Veblen, Thorstein. *The Theory of the Leisure Class.*

Vinogradoff, Paul. *Common Sense in Law.*

Voltaire. *Voltaire's Philosophical Dictionary.*

Walter, William Wilfred, ed. *The Unknown God.*

West, Herbert Faulkner. *Rebel Thought.*

Whitehead, Alfred North. *Essays in Science and Philosophy.*

Williams, Glanville. *The Sanctity of Life and the Criminal Law.*

Wilson, Ernest C. *Every Good Desire.*

POETRY

Aiken, Conrad, ed. *Twentieth-Century American Poetry.*

Browning, Robert. *The Complete Poetic and Dramatic Works of Robert Browning.*

————. *The Ring and the Book.*

————. *Men and Women.*

Dickinson, Emily. *Poems.*

Dickman, William J. *Around the Potomac.*

Donne, John and Blake, William. *The Complete Poetry and Selected Prose of John Donne and the Complete Poetry of William Blake.*

Dozier, Orion T. *A Galaxy of Southern Heroes, and Other Poems.*

————. *Poems and Prose.*

Emerson, Ralph Waldo. *The Works of Ralph Waldo Emerson.*

Frost, Robert. *A Witness Tree.*

Hood, Thomas. *Humorous Poems of Thomas Hood.*

Houser, Terzah Adams. *Into the Sunlight.*

Kipling, Rudyard. *The Recessional, The Vampire, and Other Poems.*

Kronenberger, Louis, ed. *An Anthology of Light Verse.*

Lynch, Harriet P. *A Year Book of Southern Poets.*

MacLeish, Archibald. *America Was Promises.*

McCorvey, Thomas Chalmers. *Alabama Historical Poems.*

Meek, Alexander Beaufort. *The Red Eagle: A Poem of the South.*

Millay, Edna St. Vincent. *The Harp-Weaver and Other Poems.*

Miyamori, Asatarō, tr. and annotator. *An Anthology of Japanese Poems.*

Monroe, Harriet and Zabel, Morton D., eds. *A Book of Poems for Every Mood.*

Moore, Thomas. *The Poetical Works of Thomas Moore, With Explanatory Notes, Etc.*

More Heart Throbs.

Nash, Ogden. *Versus.*

Pike, Albert. *Hymns to the Gods and Other Poems.*

Ryan, Abram J. *Father Ryan's Poems.*

Sandburg, Carl. *Remembrance Rock.*

Shakespeare, William. (See ENGLISH LITERATURE).

Simms, William Gilmore. *War Poetry of the South.*

Stirling, Sarah Vowell Daingerfield. *Thoughts.*

Sullivan, Aloysius Michael. *The Bottom of the Sea.*

Yeats, William Butler. *The Collected Poems of W. B. Yeats.*

————. *Wheels and Butterflies.*

REFERENCE WORKS

Allen, Frederic Sturges. *Synonyms and Antonyms.*

The American College Dictionary.

Bartlett, John. *Familiar Quotations.*

Benet, William Rose, ed. *The Reader's Encyclopedia.*

Canby, Henry Seidel and Opdycke, John Baker. *Handbook of English Usage.*

Declaration of Independence and Constitution of The United States of America.

Eichler, Lillian. *The New Book of Etiquette.*

Encyclopaedia Britannica. *Book of the Year: 1968.*

———. *Book of the Year: 1969.*

———. *Encyclopaedia Britannica.* 11th edition.

———. *Encyclopaedia Britannica.* 1968 edition.

———. *World Atlas.*

Fernald, James Champlin. *English Synonyms, Antonyms, With Notes on the Correct Use of Prepositions.*

Fryer, Douglas and Henry, Edwin R. *An Outline of General Psychology.*

Funk, Wilfred and Lewis, Norman. *Thirty Days to a More Powerful Vocabulary.*

Johnson, Allen, ed. *Dictionary of American Biography.*

Mawson, Christopher Orlando Sylvester, ed. *Roget's International Thesaurus of English Words and Phrases.*

Merck, George. *Merck Manual of Diagnosis and Therapy.* 4 editions.

———. *Merck Manual of Therapeutics and Materia Medica: A Source of Ready Reference for the Physician.*

Physicians' Desk Reference to Pharmaceutical Specialities and Biologicals.

Rand McNally. *Ideal Atlas of the World.*

———. *Road Atlas: U.S., Canada, Mexico.* 2 copies.

Robinson, Victor. *The New People's Physician: The Concise Encyclopedia of Health.*

Runes, Dagobert D., ed. *Dictionary of Philosophy: Ancient, Medieval, Modern.*

Voltaire. *Voltaire's Philosophical Dictionary.*

Walsh, William S. *International Encyclopedia of Prose and Poetical Quotations.*

Webster, Noah. *Webster's New International Dictionary.*

World Geographic Atlas: A Composite of Man's Environment.

ROME

Appian. *Appian's Roman History.*

Baring-Gould, S[abine]. *The Tragedy of the Caesars.*

Carcopino, Jérôme. *Cicero: The Secrets of His Correspondence.*

Cicero, Marcus Tullius. *Brutus; On the Nature of the Gods; On Divination; On Duties.*

———. *De Republica de Legibus.*

Epicurus. *Epicurus' Morals, Collected Partly Out of His Own Greek Text, in Diogenes Laertius, and Partly Out of the Rhapsodies of Marcus Antonius, Plutarch, Cicero and Seneca.*

Gibbon, Edward. *The History of the Decline and Fall of the Roman Empire.*

Graves, Robert. *I, Claudius: From the Autobiography of Tiberius Claudius, Born B.C. 10, Murdered and Deified A.D. 54.*

Grimal, Pierre. *The Civilization of Rome.*

Hamilton, Edith. *The Roman Way.*

Haskell, H[enry] J[oseph]. *This Was Cicero: Modern Politics in a Roman Toga.*

Josephus, Flavius. *The Works of Flavius Josephus . . . .*

Junius [pseudonym]. *Stat Nominis Umbra.*

Livy [Titus Livius]. *The History of Rome.*

Lucretius. *T. Lucreti Cari, De Rerum Natura.*

Mahaffy, John Pentland, ed. *History of Rome and of the Roman People.*

Middleton, Conyers. *The History of the Life of Marcus Tullius Cicero.*

Milman, Henry. *Life of Quintus Horatius Flaccus.*

Seneca, [Lucius Annaeus]. *The Morals of Seneca: A Selection of His Prose.*

———. *Seneca's Morals: By Way of Abstract, to Which is Added a Discourse Under the Title of an After-Thought.*

Suetonius [C. Suetonius Tranquillus]. *The Lives of the Twelve Caesars.*

Tacitus, Cornelius. *The Works of Cornelius Tacitus . . . .*

———. *The Works of Tacitus: The Annals.*

Terence. *The Comedies of Terence.*

Walford, Edward. *Juvenal.*

THE SOUTH

Alderman, Edwin Anderson and Gordon, Armistead Churchill. *J. L. M. Curry: A Biography.*

Allen, Ivan. *Atlanta From the Ashes.*

Ashmore, Harry S. *An Epitaph for Dixie.*

Baldwin, Joseph G. *The Flush Times of Alabama and Mississippi: A Series of Sketches.*

Botkin, Benjamin Albert, ed. *A Treasury of Southern Folklore: Stories, Ballads, Traditions and Folkways of the People of the South.*

Bowers, Claude G. *The Tragic Era: The Revolution After Lincoln.* 3 copies.

Campbell, Thomas Monroe. *The Movable School Goes to the Negro Farmer.*

Chandler, Julian Alvin Carroll, ed. *The South in the Building of the Nation.*

Claiborne, J[ohn] F[rancis] H[amtramck]. *Life and Correspondence of John A. Quitman, Major-General, U.S.A., and Governor of the State of Mississippi.*

Curry, J[abez] L[amar] M[onroe]. *Civil History of the Government of the Confederate States, With Some Personal Reminiscences.*

——. *The Southern States of the American Union, Considered in Their Relations to the Constitution of the United States and to the Resulting Union.* 2 copies.

Dabbs, James McBride. *The Southern Heritage.*

Dodd, William E. *Statesmen of the Old South, or, From Radicalism to Conservative Revolt.*

Dozier, Orion T. *A Galaxy of Southern Heroes, and Other Poems.*

DuBose, John Witherspoon. *The Life and Times of William Lowndes Yancey.*

Dykeman, Wilma and Stokely, James. *Seeds of Southern Change: The Life of Will Alexander.*

Elkins, Stanley M. *Slavery.*

Fleming, Walter L. *Civil War and Reconstruction in Alabama.* 2 copies.

Gaston, Paul M. *The New South Creed: A Study in Southern Mythmaking.*

Graves, John Temple. *The Fighting South.*

Harris, Joel Chandler, ed. *Life of Henry W. Grady, Including His Writings and Speeches.*

Henry, Robert Selph. *The Story of the Confederacy.*

Hill, Benjamin Harvey, Jr. *Senator Benjamin H. Hill of Georgia: His Life Speeches and Writings.*

Horne, Ida Caroline Harrell. *Simple Southern Songs.*

Howard, Henry Jacob. *From These Roots: The Story of North Greenville Junior College, 1892–1967.*

Key, V[aldimer] O[rlando], Jr. *Southern Politics in State and Nation.*

King, Martin Luther, Jr. *Stride Toward Freedom: The Montgomery Story.*

[Longstreet, Augustus Baldwin]. *Georgia Scenes, Characters, Incidents, Etc., in the First Half Century of the Republic, by a Native Georgian.*

Lynch, Harriet P. *A Year Book of Southern Poets.*

Meade, Robert Douthat. *Judah P. Benjamin: Confederate Statesman.*

Meek, Alexander Beaufort. *The Red Eagle: A Poem of the South.*

Michie, Allan A. and Ryhlick, Frank. *Dixie Demagogues.*

Nixon, Herman Clarence. *Forty Acres and Steel Mules.*

Osterweis, Rollin G. *Romanticism and Nationalism in the Old South.*

Pickett, Albert James. *History of Alabama, and Incidentally of Georgia and Mississippi, From the Earliest Period.*

Richardson, James D., comp. *A Compilation of the Messages and Papers of the Confederacy.*

Ryan, Abram J. *Father Ryan's Poems.*

Sandlapper 1968: The Magazine of South Carolina.

Simkins, Francis Butler. *The South: Old and New, A History, 1820–1947.*

Simms, William Gilmore. *War Poetry of the South.*

Sindler, Allan P., ed. *Change in the Contemporary South.*

Skaggs, William H. *The Southern Oligarchy: An Appeal in Behalf of the Silent Masses of Our Country Against the Despotic Rule of the Few.*

Sloss, Edith Tyndale. *Echoes of the Old Plantation.*

Strode, Hudson. *Jefferson Davis: Confederate President.*

Walker, Anne Kendrick. *Braxton Bragg Comer: His Family Tree From Virginia's Colonial Days.*

Whisnant, Charleen. *Red Clay Reader.*

Williams, T. Harry. *Huey Long.*

Woodward, C. Vann. *Origins of the New South, 1877–1913.*

——. *The South in Search of a Philosophy.*

TENNIS

Buchanan, Lamont. *The Story of Tennis.*

Budge, J. Donald. *Budge on Tennis.*

Budge, Lloyd. *Tennis Made Easy.*

Harman, Bob and Monroe, Keith. *Use Your Head in Tennis.*

Jacobs, Helen Hull. *The Young Sportsman's Guide to Tennis.*

Lardner, Rex. *The Underhanded Serve, or How to Play Dirty Tennis.*

Ramo, Simon. *Extraordinary Tennis for the Ordinary Player: Winning Strategy for the Tennis Enthusiast Who Plays for Fun.*

Talbert, William F. *Tennis Observed: Photos and Stories About Early Tennis Players.*

Vines, Ellsworth. *How to Play Better Tennis.*

WORLD HISTORY

Churchill, Winston S. *The Grand Alliance: The Second World War*.
Durant, Will and Ariel. *The Lessons of History*.
Emerson, Edwin, Jr. *A History of the Nineteenth Century Year by Year*.
Hoyland, John S. *They Saw Gandhi*.
Lord, John. *Beacon Lights of History*.
Quigley, Carroll. *The Evolution of Civilizations*.
de Santillana, Giorgio. *The Crime of Galileo*.
Toynbee, Arnold J. *A Study of History*.
Van Loon, Hendrik Willem. *The Story of Mankind*.
Wells, H[erbert] G[eorge]. *The Outline of History*.

Mr. Justice Black's
Law Clerks and Staff

Mr. Justice Black's Law Clerks and Staff

Law Clerks

Term	Clerks	Home State at Time of Appointment	Law School
1937	Jerome A. Cooper	Ala.	Harvard
1938	Jerome A. Cooper	Ala.	Harvard
1939	Jerome A. Cooper	Ala.	Harvard
1940	Marx Leva	Ala.	Harvard
1941	Max Isenberg	N.Y.	Harvard
1942	Chris J. Dixie*	Texas	Texas
	John P. Frank	Wisc.	Wisconsin, Yale
1943	Charles F. Luce	Wisc.	Wisconsin, Yale
1944	Sidney M. Davis	N.Y.	Chicago
1945	David Haber	N.Y.	Yale
1946	Louis F. Oberdorfer	Ala.	Yale
1947	William Joslin	N.C.	Columbia
1948	Truman Hobbs	Ala.	Yale
1949	Frank M. Wozencraft	D.C.	Yale
1950	Luther L. Hill, Jr.	Ala.	Harvard
	George M. Treister	Calif.	Yale
1951	C. Sam Daniels	Fla.	Columbia
	Neal P. Rutledge	Md.	Yale
1952	Melford O. Cleveland	Ala.	Alabama, Yale
	Huey B. Howerton, Jr.†	Miss.	Mississippi, Yale
1953	Charles A. Reich	N.Y.	Yale
	David J. Vann	Ala.	Alabama, Geo. Wash.
1954	Daniel J. Meador	Ala.	Alabama, Harvard
	James W. H. Stewart	Ala.	Wash. & Lee, Harvard
1955	J. Vernon Patrick	Ala.	Harvard
	Harold A. Ward, III	Fla.	Chicago
1956	George C. Freeman, Jr.	Ala.	Yale
	Robert A. Girard	Wash.	Harvard
1957	David M. Clark	N.C.	N.Y.U.
	Robert A. Girard	Wash.	Harvard
1958	Robert T. Basseches*	N.Y.	Yale
	Guido Calabresi	Conn.	Yale
	David M. Clark	N.C.	N.Y.U.
1959	Nicholas Johnson	Texas	Texas
	John K. McNulty	N.Y.	Yale

Term	Clerks	Home State at Time of Appointment	Law School
1960	George L. Saunders, Jr.	Ala.	Chicago
	Lawrence G. Wallace	N.Y.	Columbia
1961	Floyd F. Feeney	N.C.	N.Y.U.
	George L. Saunders, Jr.	Ala.	Chicago
1962	A. E. Dick Howard	Va.	Virginia
	Clay C. Long	Ala.	Harvard
1963	A. E. Dick Howard	Va.	Virginia
	John G. Kester	Wisc.	Harvard
1964	John G. Kester	Wisc.	Harvard
	James L. North	Ala.	Virginia
1965	Drayton Nabers, Jr.	Ala.	Yale
	John W. Vardaman, Jr.	Ala.	Harvard
1966	Margaret J. Corcoran†	D.C.	Harvard
	Stephen D. Susman	Texas	Texas
1967	Joseph H. Price	Ala.	Harvard
	Stephen J. Schulhofer	N.Y.	Harvard
1968	Walter E. Dellinger, III	N.C.	Yale
	Stephen J. Schulhofer	N.Y.	Harvard
1969	Kenneth C. Bass, III	Va.	Yale
	G. Marshall Moriarty**	Mass.	Harvard
	J. Gustave Speth, Jr.	S.C.	Yale
1970	John M. Harmon**	N.C.	Duke
	Robert B. McCaw	Va.	Virginia
	Robert W. Spearman	N.C.	Yale
1971	Larry Hammond*	Texas	Texas
	John M. Harmon*	N.C.	Duke
	Covert Eugene Parnell, III*	Ala.	Harvard

*Part-year.
**Assigned to Justice Black by the Chief Justice for a portion of the term.
†Deceased.

Secretaries

1937–1946	Anne Butt Daniel
1946–1956	Gladys B. Coates
1956–1957	Elizabeth Seay DeMeritte
1957–1971	Frances L. Lamb

Messenger

1937–1971	Spencer C. Campbell